A Redwood Forest, California

PLANT ECOLOGY

BY

W. B. McDOUGALL

PROFESSOR OF BOTANY IN THE UNIVERSITY OF SOUTHERN CALIFORNIA,
LOS ANGELES, CALIF.

SECOND EDITION, THOROUGHLY REVISED

ILLUSTRATED WITH 120 ENGRAVINGS

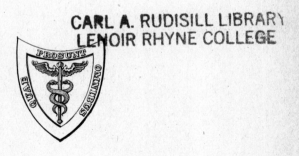

LEA & FEBIGER
PHILADELPHIA
1931

Copyright

LEA & FEBIGER

1931

TO

MY THREE DAUGHTERS

PREFACE TO THE SECOND EDITION.

THE reception accorded the first edition of this book has been most gratifying. In this, the second, edition the same order of presentation has been followed but the material has been carefully revised in order to bring it up to date. An article on atmospheric humidity has been added in Chapter XII and briefer additions have been made in various places throughout the book. Several new illustrations have also been included. A number of new references to literature have been added, but the policy, adopted in the first edition, of listing only some of the more important of the recent literature in the English language has been retained.

The author is very grateful for the suggestions that have come to him from users of the book and solicits equally frank expressions concerning this edition.

W. B. McD.

LOS ANGELES, CALIF.

PREFACE TO THE FIRST EDITION.

THE science of plant ecology has been badly in need of a text-book for a number of years. While there are many valuable books on various phases of the science there has been no single book in the English language that covered the subject in such a way that it could be used as a text in a comprehensive beginning course. The need of a text-book has been recognized for some time but the very rapid growth of the science has resulted in a great deal of disagreement about certain rather fundamental principles and has made the production of a book that would not be subject to severe criticism seemingly impossible.

The present volume is an attempt to supply the need of a text-book of plant ecology. Criticisms of it will be welcomed and are hereby solicited, for in the criticisms will lie the greatest hope of a better book in the future. The book is based on a course of lectures that has been given for several years to beginning classes in plant ecology at the University of Illinois. It is hoped that it will prove useful in other universities and, more especially, in colleges and normal schools where plant ecology is, or should be, taught. The text has purposely been made brief and probably many ecologists will not agree that a happy choice has always been made in deciding what to include and what to leave out. The entire field of plant ecology is covered, however, and as much material is included as can be given in a half year course with two lectures a week.

References to ecological literature are given at the ends of the chapters. No attempt has been made to include complete bibliographies on any subject. For the most part only some of the more recent publications are listed, very few that were published more than ten years ago being included. Usually the bibliographies in the publications listed will enable anyone to go much deeper into the literature of any phase of ecology in which he may be interested. An appendix, giving some suggestions concerning laboratory and field work, is added in response to numerous requests that have come from teachers for such information.

The author is very greatly indebted to Miss Winona H. Welch, Miss Margaret C. Jacobs, and Mr. W. C. Croxton all of whom have read the entire manuscript and have aided greatly in eliminating typographical errors, crudities in English and errors in the statements of facts. All illustrations obtained from individuals or used by permission of publishing companies are acknowledged in the legends of the figures. Illustrations not so acknowledged are by the author. Naturally, free use has been made of the published statements of numerous ecologists for which individual acknowledgement is not attempted. Sincere thanks are hereby expressed to all who have aided in any way, directly or indirectly, in the preparation or publication of the book.

W. B. McD.

Urbana, Illinois.

CONTENTS.

(xi)

PLANT ECOLOGY.

CHAPTER I.

INTRODUCTION.

MAN could not live without plants. They are the source of all food, practically all fuel, and all important fibers except wool and silk which are obtained from animals that feed upon plants. They are also the direct source of rubber, paper, most drugs, and very many other products without which the progress of civilization would have been absolutely impossible. There can be no question of the desirability of studying objects that are of such very great importance to our health and comfort, indeed to our very existence, as are plants.

1. **The Necessity of Studying Plants in the Field.**—Plants have been objects of study for a very long time. Too often in recent times the studies have been confined largely to laboratories and books while field studies have been neglected.

The only practical way to become well acquainted with plants is to study them where they grow. The botanist who has limited himself largely to laboratory and library studies is usually considerably at a loss when he faces a field problem. He does not recognize the different kinds of plants nor does he know where to look for particular kinds nor why these kinds cannot be expected to grow in certain types of places. Many of the most important plant problems awaiting solution at the present time, problems that are of vital importance to the world's food supply or to the supply

2

of lumber and other forest products, are field problems. It is, therefore, essential that those who are training themselves along botanical lines should place a reasonable emphasis upon field work.

There is another reason for studying plants in the field that must receive consideration. This has to do with the esthetic value of plants. None of us would care to live in a house around which there were absolutely no plants. Whenever we think of a beautiful home or a beautiful city we think of one that is well supplied with trees, shrubs, grass and flowers. The beauty of plants in such places is greatest when their arrangements are similar to those found in Nature. Thus if we would make the best esthetic use of our plants we must study in the field the ways in which Nature makes use of the same or similar plants. A full appreciation of the beauties of Nature can be realized only by those who understand the reasons for the natural groupings of plants that are found.

2. **What Plant Ecology Is.**—Ecology is the science of the interrelations of living things and their environments. Plant ecology then is the science of the interrelations of plants and their environments. It has sometimes been called, not inaptly, plant sociology. It is essentially a field study and this fact distinguishes it from plant morphology and plant physiology which are essentially laboratory studies. It is one of the most practical of the subdivisions of botany, since ecological principles form the basis of practice in agriculture and forestry. The ecologist has up to the present time worked out the majority of his problems through the use of wild plants, but this has been only because of convenience. The problems of the practical plant grower and those of the ecologist are similar and often identical. They are concerned always with the relations of the plant to its environment.

3. **The Environment of Plants.**—The environment of a plant consists of everything outside of the plant which

influences in any way the life of the plant. The environment is partly living and partly non-living. The living part of the environment consists of plants and animals. The non-

FIG. 1.—Diagram showing the principal factors in the environment of land plants. (From Transeau's General Botany. Copyright 1923 by World Book Company, Yonkers-on-Hudson, New York.)

living part consists of numerous influences such as light, heat, air, soil and water. Each part of the environment which may exert a specific influence upon the life of the plant is spoken of as a factor of the environment or as an ecological factor (Fig. 1).

4. **Autecology and Synecology.**—In the study of plant ecology we find it necessary to treat not only of the relations of individual plants to the environment but also of comparable relations of communities of plants. The ecology of individual plants is called autecology while the ecology of plant communities is designated synecology.

This book covers the entire field of plant ecology but the earlier chapters deal almost entirely with autecology while the later chapters treat more largely of synecology.

CHAPTER II.

THE ECOLOGY OF ROOTS.

ROOTS are primarily the absorbing and anchoring organs of plants. Internally their structure is similar to that of stems. Externally they are distinguished from stems by the absence of nodes and internodes and especially by the absence of regularly arranged buds. They vary greatly in form and size. Some of the variations are due to inheritance while others are due to the environment and so are of ecological significance.

5. **Absorption.**—The absorption of materials from soil takes place primarily through root hairs. Root hairs are extensions of cortical cells of roots. They are ordinarily from one to several millimeters in length and so small that as many as 300 have been counted on a single square millimeter of surface, though often they are not nearly so numerous as that. The numerous root hairs increase the absorbing surface of the roots from 2 to 10 times and sometimes even more and this is probably the chief advantage of these structures. Most root hairs have cell walls which are very thin and pliable and this makes it possible for them to come into very close contact with the soil particles. They usually become very irregular in shape through this intimate contact with the soil particles and they cling to these particles so tenaciously that when roots are pulled from the soil the root hairs are for the most part broken off from the root rather than being pulled loose from the soil particles.

The ordinary thin-walled root hairs are rather ephemeral structures lasting only a few days or at most a few weeks. As a root elongates new root hairs are constantly being formed just back of the root tip and at the same time the oldest hairs farther back are dying off. There is thus an area of root hairs, rather definite in extent, which is constantly moving forward as the root elongates and so is coming into contact with fresh supplies of food materials in the soil (Fig. 2).

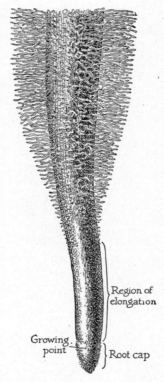

FIG. 2.—Root tip, showing root cap, growing region, and root hairs. (From Transeau's General Botany. Copyright 1923 by World Book Company, Yonkers-on-Hudson, New York.)

In the case of some plants that grow in very dry places such as deserts the root hairs become thick-walled and persist

for several months or even years. This is true also of a few
plants that grow where the water supply is abundant, such
as the honey locust (*Gleditsia triacanthos*) (Fig. 3), the
Kentucky coffee tree (*Gymnocladus dioica*), the red bud
(*Cercis canadensis*), and a number of species of the composite
family. It is probable that in all of these cases the habit

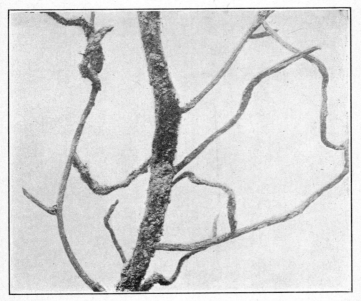

FIG. 3.—Roots of *Gleditsia triacanthos* showing persistent root hairs.

of producing thick-walled root hairs was formed at a time
when the plants concerned grew only in very dry situations.

The rate of absorption from the soil, especially of water,
depends not only upon the structural characteristics of the
root system but also upon a number of external factors.
One of these, of course, is the actual amount of water present
in the soil. If there is a deficient amount of water present
a state of physical dryness (actual absence of sufficient water)

exists and the rate of absorption is reduced.   A second factor
concerned here is temperature.   A high temperature, up
to a certain limit, increases the rate of absorption while a
low temperature decreases it.   A third factor affecting the
rate of absorption is the amount of salts, that is, of soluble
materials, in the soil.   Either a low temperature or a high
concentration of salts in the soil brings about a condition
that is spoken of as physiological dryness which means that
while there may be an adequate amount of water present
the plants cannot absorb it readily.   The reason why the
plants cannot get water readily from a salty soil is that the
concentration of the soil solution is too nearly equal to that
of the cell sap to allow the water to diffuse into the cells
rapidly.   Obviously the extent of the effect of this factor
depends upon the concentration of the cell sap, which varies
greatly in different kinds of plants.

It was formerly thought that the absorption of nutrient
materials from the soil took place almost entirely from the
surface layer to a depth of only 6 or 8 inches.   Recent experiments, however, have shown that both water and mineral
salts are absorbed from all layers of soil that are occupied
by roots.   For example, potatoes absorbed from all layers to
a depth of 2.5 feet, barley to 3 feet, and corn to 5 feet.   In
all cases somewhat larger amounts were absorbed from the
upper layers but this was probably due only to the presence
of larger numbers of roots in those layers.   These facts are
very important in connection with the addition of artificial
fertilizers to soils in which crop plants are to be grown.

6. **Anchorage.**—While the function of absorption is limited
largely to the smallest roots and especially to the root hairs,
anchorage is a function of the entire root system.   That
root systems in general are efficient in performing this function is shown by the infrequency with which plants are
uprooted by the wind.   It is seldom that even tall trees
are uprooted except when a region is visited by a tornado.
Experiments have shown that healthy corn plants four

months old will offer a resistance of 200 to 360 pounds to a straight vertical pull. The efficiency of the root system is well seen also along streams where the banks are being eroded by the water. The root system of a tree may be more than half uncovered and still hold the plant upright.

Where trees are growing along streams erosion is much less rapid than where there are few or no plants as the roots tend to hold the soil in place (Fig. 4). In fact usually the

Fig. 4.—Trees and shrubs checking erosion on a hillside.

simplest way to check erosion in such a place is to plant trees or shrubs. This is equally true of other places where erosion is likely to occur, such as hillsides. Some kinds of plants are much more efficient than others in holding the soil. In sandy regions and especially in regions of shifting sand dunes, such as occur along sea coasts, there are certain plants, particularly some kinds of grasses, that are known as "sand binders" because of their ability to grow in the unstable sand and often to check its movements or even to stop it entirely (Fig. 5). The movement of the sand in such a place is of course due to wind action and the sand-binding plants are often planted along railroads and the borders of farms to prevent the encroachment of the sand through the agency of wind.

FIG. 5.—*Hudsonia tomentosa.* A sand binding plant. (Photograph by A. G. Eldredge.)

7. Food Accumulation.—Many plants have thick fleshy roots which serve the somewhat special function of store houses for accumulated foods. This is especially true of plants with tap roots such as beets, parsnips and dandelions. It is also true of many plants with fascicled or tuberous roots, as the dahlia and the sweet potato.

Most of these storage roots accumulate starch and in some, the sweet potato for example, there is not much except starch. Some however, like the beet, accumulate sugar in addition to starch, and the dandelion and dahlia as well as many other members of the composite family accumulate considerable quantities of inulin, a soluble carbohydrate.

Practically all of these thickened roots also accumulate water and in many cases this is more important than the accumulation of food. Many desert plants have immense root systems which store up water in great quantities and the plants depend upon these supplies during rainless seasons.

Roots have obvious advantages as storage organs because of their position. They are better protected from animals than are aërial organs and are somewhat protected also from extremes of temperature or, perhaps of more importance, from sudden changes of temperature. Furthermore, and of still greater importance, they are very well protected from desiccation.

8. **Growth and Development.**—Certain factors in the environment of roots are more constant than corresponding factors in the environment of aërial organs. This is especially true of temperature. Some other factors, however, are as variable below the surface of the soil as above it. In the case of plants that live only during one season the roots ordinarily grow continuously from the time the seed germinates until the plant dies, although the rate of growth varies greatly from time to time as the factors of the environment, such as temperature and water supply, become more or less favorable. The roots of plants that live more than one year ordinarily cease growth at certain times during each year, at least in regions having warm and cold or wet and dry seasons. These periods of growth cessation are spoken of as "rest periods" though, of course, the roots are never actually in need of rest from growth. The cause of these rest periods is lack of sufficient water for growth. In the case of forest trees in the temperate zones, for instance, there is always a rest period in winter when the soil becomes physiologically dry through low temperature, and in a dry year there may also be a rest period in summer when the soil becomes physically dry. In a wet year, however, the roots of trees grow throughout the summer and this is probably

the rule every year in the case of those roots that are so deep in the soil that the water supply never becomes inadequate.

The characteristics of a root system as to shape and extent depend in part upon inheritance and in part upon the environment. Practically all roots tend to grow toward water unless there is some inhibiting factor such as absence of oxygen or presence of a toxic substance. In a wet soil the majority of the roots are apt to be near the surface while in a dry soil they extend much deeper. It has been found that in sand-dune regions different species of plants may react quite differently to variations in the soil resulting from buried deposits of organic matter. The growth of some kinds of roots is increased by these deposits while other kinds of roots may be unaffected or their growth may even be inhibited.

In the case of several crop plants it has been found that the presence of fertilizers in the soil promotes vigorous growth and profuse branching of the roots. Considerable increases in yield of the potato crop have been obtained in certain regions by working fertilizers into the surface layer of soil and then plowing about 9 inches deep before planting the potatoes. The deep placing of the fertilizers causes the roots to develop abundantly in the deeper layers. If, then, there is a dry season while the crop is developing, and the surface layers of soil dry out, the plants are not affected as they would be if the greater numbers of roots were in the surface layers.

9. **Aëration and Root Growth.**—Roots carry on respiration just as all other parts of the plant do. In this process they use up oxygen and excrete carbon dioxide. Therefore, either a deficiency of oxygen or an excessive accumulation of carbon dioxide is injurious to the root system. The commonest condition that results in a deficiency of oxygen is the presence of an excessive amount of water in the soil. When the soil is saturated with water, air cannot get in and a prolonged saturation often causes crop plants actually to drown. These

facts need to be taken into consideration wherever irrigation is carried on. Undoubtedly in many, if not in most, places where irrigation is practiced too much water has commonly been used. The plants need both water and air and it is necessary for best results to strike a compromise between these two needs.

In swamps where the soil is constantly saturated with water the majority of roots grow horizontally rather than downward and sometimes even grow vertically upward. This is notably characteristic of the bald cypress tree which produces upright branches from horizontal roots which are called cypress knees; but this phenomenon is characteristic of many plants besides the cypress.

In peat bogs the conditions for aëration seem to be particularly bad. Such a place is practically if not entirely undrained and the deep layers of peat, constantly saturated with water, prevent the entrance of oxygen and facilitate the accumulation of carbon dioxide. The acidity that results from this accumulation of carbon dioxide brings about a condition of physiological dryness. Under such conditions many plants which flourish in ordinary swamps cannot grow at all. Many plants which are found in peat bogs have structural features that are characteristic of dry land plants and this has been attributed largely to the physiological dryness of the bog.

10. **Root Duration.**—Some roots live for only a few weeks or months while others, as those of some trees, may live for hundreds of years. The classification of plants into annuals, biennials and perennials is based largely upon the length of life of the parts within the soil, though not in all cases on roots. An annual plant is one that completes its life cycle within one vegetative season; a biennial one that lives during part or all of two vegetative seasons; and a perennial one that lives during more than two vegetative seasons. In many biennial plants, such as the parsnip, practically the only part that lives through the winter is the root. Many

perennials, also, are annual above ground and live through
the winter below ground. Some of these have perennial
underground stems and in these the roots may be, and often
are, annual, while others have perennial roots. Woody plants
are perennial both above and below the surface of the soil.

Some plants may be annuals or biennials depending upon
the time of germination. Spring wheat, for example, is
an annual while winter wheat is a biennial. Some plants,
likewise, that are annuals when grown in periodic climates
may be perennials in uniform climates. The castor bean
grows in Florida, for example, as a perennial and becomes a
small tree, while in the northern part of the United States
it is an annual.

11. **The Position of Roots in the Soil.**—We have already
spoken of certain variations in depth and extent of root
systems due to conditions of the environment. The position
in the soil of the roots of any particular kind of plant, however, is governed in part also by inheritance. A maple
tree, for instance, practically always produces a large number
of roots in the surface layer of the soil. This is one of the
main reasons why it is so difficult to get lawn grass to grow
under a maple tree. On the other hand an oak tree growing
under exactly similar conditions has a much smaller number
of surface roots. Again, a corn plant, at germination,
produces a primary root system from the seed and a more
extensive root system is formed later by adventitious roots
from the lower part of the stem. This latter root system is
always produced at approximately the same depth whether
the corn has been planted relatively shallow or very deep.

In a community of plants where a large number of kinds
are growing together it is usually found that they vary greatly
in the depths of the main parts of their root systems (Fig. 6).
This is distinctly advantageous since it makes it possible
for a much greater number of plants to occupy the area
than would be the case if they all had their roots at the same
level. A similar response to depth is found in underground

stems. The underground stem of any particular kind of plant is always at approximately the same distance below the surface of the soil. If soil is piled up above the growing tip of such a stem it grows upward until it reaches the normal distance from the surface. Likewise, if soil is dug away from before it, or if it encounters a natural depression, it grows downward until it reaches its usual depth. This phenomenon, which is not well understood, has been spoken of as the "law of level."

Of considerable interest in connection with the position of roots in the soil is the phenomenon of root contraction. This again is not well understood but it is rather common nevertheless. A dandelion is often spoken of as a stemless plant. It, of course, is not stemless. It has a short stem at the surface of the soil and the stem bears the leaves. This stem increases in length a little each year but, although the plant may live for many years, it never becomes any taller because every year the root contracts enough to pull the stem down as much as it has grown upward.

12. **Roots and Transplanting.**—When the end of a growing root is cut off an excessive number of branches is ordinarily produced back of the cut. It is possible therefore to produce a compact and dense root system by cutting off the ends of all of the longer roots of a plant. Shrubs and trees that have been grown in a nursery usually do better than transplanted native plants because in the nursery stock compact root systems have been induced by frequent transplanting. At each transplanting the longer roots are cut off and thus at the final and permanent transplanting there is a minimum of disturbance of the root system. Even large trees may be successfully transplanted if their preparation for it is begun a year or two in advance. The preparation consists of gradually cutting off the roots a few feet from the base of the tree and loosening the soil near the tree so that a large number of short absorbing branches are produced. When

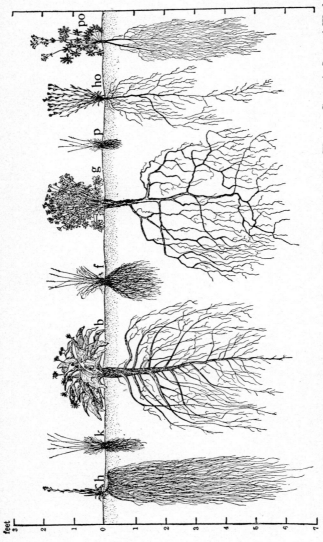

FIG. 6.—Bisect showing root systems of prairie plants at different levels (After Weaver, Carnegie Inst. of Washington, 1919). Drawn from photographs and data obtained by the excavation and examination of 325 rootsystems of these 8 species: *h, Hieracium scouleri; k, Koeleria cristata; b, Balsamorhiza sagittata; f, Festuca ovina ingrata; g, Geranium viscosissimum; p, Poa sandbergii; ho, Hoorebekia racemosa; po, Potentilla blaschkeana.*

the tree is finally transplanted these branches are ready to begin at once the work of absorption.

13. **Water Roots.**—Roots of floating plants which grow entirely in water are much less extensively developed than are soil roots. There are usually few if any branches and no root hairs. Some floating plants have no roots at all, absorption taking place through stems or leaves. *Salvinia,* the water fern, for example, has two kinds of leaves, broad flat ones which float on the surface, and elongated, much dissected ones which hang down into the water like roots and perform the function of absorption. The duckweed, *Wolffia,* although it is a seed plant, has neither roots, stems, nor leaves but consists of a small football-shaped thallus through the entire surface of which absorption may take place. *Lemna,* another duckweed, has a single unbranched root only a few millimeters in length, while *Spirodela* has several such roots.

Water plants which have roots extending into the soil are intermediate between ordinary soil plants and floating plants in the relative development of their root systems. When the roots of such plants are growing in water they ordinarily remain unbranched but if they extend into the soil they branch freely and produce root hairs like ordinary soil roots.

14. **Air Roots.**—Air roots like water roots are relatively unbranched and without root hairs. Some climbing plants, such as poison ivy and Virginia creeper, produce innumerable air roots which grow horizontally around the support and so serve as anchoring roots. Such roots probably do not perform the function of absorption at all.

In corn and a number of other monocotyledonous plants roots are produced at some of the lower aërial nodes of the stem. These grow obliquely downward as unbranched air roots until they reach the soil. After entering the soil they branch freely and serve an important function as prop roots. In the banyan tree roots grow vertically downward and into the soil from horizontal branches. These roots become stiff

3

and form a system of supports which make it possible for a single tree to continue to spread until it covers an enormous area.

Many tropical orchids which grow upon the branches of other plants where the conditions for absorption are difficult have specially modified air roots (Fig. 7). These roots are usually shining white. Structurally they differ from ordinary roots by having a layer several cells thick outside of the

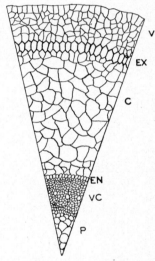

FIG. 7.—Sector of a cross-section of an air root of an orchid. *V*, velamen; *Ex*, exodermis; *C*, cortex; *En*, endodermis; *VC*, vascular tissue; *P*, pith.

cortex. This is called the velamen and it absorbs water with great rapidity by capillarity whenever dew or rain comes in contact with it. Between the velamen and the cortex there is a single layer of cells, the exodermis, the cell walls of which, in most cases, are more or less thickened. Some cells in this layer, however, called transfusion cells, have thin walls, and probably serve as passageways for water from the velamen into the cortex.

15. **Rhizoids.**—Roots are strictly organs of sporophytes. Gametophytes never have true roots but are supplied instead, in many cases, with rhizoids. Rhizoids are filamentous structures only one cell thick. In fern prothalli and in liverworts they are usually unicellular and unbranched while in mosses they are branched and multicellular but still only one cell thick. Many of the large marine algæ and some lichens are attached to the substratum by rhizoids. All rhizoids serve as anchorage organs and many are probably also of value in absorption.

The anchorage organs of most lichens are called rhizines and are not single filaments but are composed of a large number of filaments grown together. Their functions are the same as those of rhizoids and roots.

REFERENCES.

Church, Margaret B.: Root Contraction. Plant World, 1919, **22**, 337–340.

Clements, Frederic E.: Aëration and Air Content, the Role of Oxygen in Root Activity, Carnegie Inst. Washington Publ., 1921, **315**, 183.

Coulter, J. M., Barnes, C. E. and Cowles, H. C.: A Text-book of Botany. Vol. II. Ecology. Chapter I. Roots and Rhizoids, American Book Company, 1911.

Hulbert, James R. and Koehler, Benjamin: Anchorage and Extent of Corn Root Systems, Jour. Agric. Res., 1924, **27**, 71–78.

McDougall, W. B.: The Growth of Forest Tree Roots, Am. Jour. Bot., 1916, **3**, 384–392.

McDougall, W. B.: Thick-walled Root Hairs of Gleditsia and Related Genera, Am. Jour. Bot., 1921, **8**, 171–175.

Waterman, W. G.: Development of Roots Under Dune Conditions, Bot. Gaz., 1919, **68**, 22–53.

Weaver, J. E.: The Ecological Relations of Roots, Carnegie Inst. Washington Publ., 1919, **286**, 128.

Weaver, J. E.: Root Development of Field Crops. McGraw-Hill Book Company, 1926.

Weaver, John E and Bruner, William E.: Root Development of Vegetable Crops, McGraw-Hill Book Company, 1927.

Weaver, J. E., Jean, F. C. and Crist, J. W.: Development and Activity of Roots of Crop Plants: A Study in Crop Ecology, Carnegie Inst. Washington Publ., 1922, **316**, 117.

Whitaker, E. S.: Root Hairs and Secondary Thickening in the Compositae, Bot. Gaz., 1923, **76**, 30–38.

CHAPTER III.

THE ECOLOGY OF STEMS.

UPRIGHT stems are largely concerned with the display of foliage and with the conduction of food materials from roots to leaves and of foods from the leaves to growing regions and to storage organs. Prostrate and other horizontal stems often have the more special function of vegetative reproduction. Stems may also serve as storage organs.

16. **Foliage Display.**—The efficiency of stems as organs of foliage display depends largely upon their ability to elongate and to branch. The direction of growth of both main shoots and branches is controlled largely by gravity and light. The amount of elongation is controlled partly by light and partly by water.

One of the most efficient types of stem systems from this point of view is that of excurrent trees well exemplified by pines and spruces (Fig. 8). In such trees the shape is that of a cone, the lowermost branches being the longest and the uppermost the shortest. Leaves are borne only near the ends of these branches so that the whole forms a sort of conical tent the walls of which are formed of green leaves. Such a stem system makes possible the display of an enormous number of leaves nearly all of which receive sufficient light to enable them to carry on a maximum amount of food manufacture.

There are many other types of stem systems which are nearly as efficient as those of the excurrent trees. Herbaceous plants exhibit a great variety of forms many of them resembling those of trees. In places where these herbaceous plants are not shaded by larger plants they are fully as

(36)

efficient as trees except that because of their smaller size they cannot display so large a number of leaves.

17. **Vegetative Reproduction.**—Vegetative reproduction in the higher plants takes place almost entirely by means of stems. The commonest and most efficient type of stem from this point of view is the rhizome, or underground stem. In some kinds of plants, such as most ferns, the rhizome

Fig. 8.—A pine tree, showing excurrent type of branching.

constitutes the whole stem system of the plant. In others there are annual aërial stems which bear the leaves. Some rhizomes are practically unbranched while others branch quite extensively. In any case it is characteristic of rhizomes that they elongate each year and so advance into new territory. Frequently the older parts die off each year about as rapidly as the newer parts elongate and this, in the case of

branched rhizomes, results in the multiplication of individuals. This multiplication of individuals is not so important, however, as the advance into new territory. The
fact that the rhizome is underground makes it possible for
it to advance into an area that is already occupied by plants
almost as readily as into one that is not so occupied. This
is clearly shown whenever a field is plowed and then left
undisturbed for several years. Such a field is practically
always occupied first by annual plants but within a few years
the annual plants are crowded out and replaced by perennial
plants which have entered for the most part by means of
rhizomes. The conquest of such an area through the agency
of seeds would take much longer because it is so difficult
for the seeds to get down to the soil through a plant cover.

Runners are very much like rhizomes except that they
grow above the surface of the soil. They are not so common
nor so efficient as rhizomes, although some plants, such as
strawberries, are able to spread very rapidly by means of
runners. Somewhat similar to runners, at least in function,
are such stems as those of the raspberry which bend over
and take root at the tip and send up new shoots. Stem
tubers, which are short and very much thickened rhizomes;
corms, which are short and thick but vertical underground
stems; and bulbs which are large buds with very thick bud
scales; are all of some importance in vegetative reproduction
but are more important as storage organs.

18. **Conductive Tissues.**—The conducting elements in the
higher plants are largely of four kinds: namely, tracheæ,
tracheids, sieve tubes and parenchyma. Sap passes upward
through the plant largely through tracheæ and tracheids.
It passes downward mostly through sieve tubes, while lateral
passage of sap is primarily through parenchyma tissue, such
as that found in medullary rays.

Tracheæ are syncytes; that is, each one is made up of
several cells placed end-to-end, but from which the separating
walls have disappeared. They usually have pointed ends

and are in most cases only a few centimeters in length, though sometimes they are as much as a meter or more long, especially in some climbing plants. Tracheids differ from tracheæ in being single cells. They have pointed ends like the tracheæ but are usually only a millimeter or less in length, though in some plants they are several centimeters long. Both tracheæ and tracheids function as dead empty cells. They both occur in the xylem of the fibro-vascular bundles.

Sieve tubes, which occur in the phlœm of the fibro-vascular bundles, resemble tracheæ in being syncytes; but they differ from tracheæ in functioning as living cells with protoplasmic contents, and in having perforated cross walls called sieve plates.

Water seems to be the chief external factor influencing the development of conductive tissues. The lower plants, most of which live where there is an abundance of water, if not actually in water, have no special conductive tissue. Also, conducting tissue is greatly reduced or practically absent in submerged seed plants.

In the case of amphibious plants different individuals of the same species, or even different parts of the same individual, may differ greatly in the relative amounts of conductive tissue, it being much less developed in those growing in water than in those projecting into the air. Furthermore, it is found that in land plants the maximum amount of conductive tissue occurs in those growing in very dry situations and that the moister the environment the less is this tissue developed. This effect is also seen in the annual rings in the wood of trees, much thicker rings being produced in wet years than in dry years.

The attack of a plant by a parasite usually results in an increased development of conducting tissue. This is well seen in insect galls and root tubercles as well as in stems, leaves and roots that are attacked by fungi or other plants. Such an effect might be expected since a parasitic attack increases activity and thus increases the use of water and other materials and the result of this should be comparable to the result of a lack of these materials in the environment.

19. **Mechanical Tissues.**—Mechanical or stiffening and strengthening elements in plants are mainly of three general types. These are fibers, or elongated sclerenchyma cells; sclereids, or sclerenchyma cells that are not appreciably elongated; and collenchyma, or elongated cells whose walls are not uniformly thickened but are thickened primarily at the angles.

Fibers occur both in and around phloem and in xylem. Those that occur in the phloem or bark are called bast cells while those that occur in the xylem are called wood fibers. The commercial fibers such as flax, hemp, and jute, out of which thread, twine and ropes are made, are bast fibers. The individual fibers are only 1 or 2 mm. in length but they have pointed ends and are dovetailed together in such a way as to give great strength. When mature their walls are very thick; so thick that the lumen of the cell is extremely narrow.

Sclereids are formed by the uniform thickening of the walls of ordinary parenchyma cells and are therefore more or less isodiametric. They are found in the hard shell of nuts, in the seed of the date, and in the bark of trees. Sometimes isolated sclereids occur in places where they do not seem to be of any use, as, for example, the stone cells that occur in the fruit of the pear. In the petiole of the water lily leaf peculiar star-shaped or irregularly branched sclereids are found, their branches projecting into the large air spaces (Fig. 9).

Collenchyma cells occur in many herbaceous stems, in petioles, and in young woody stems, usually just inside the epidermis. They are living cells, often contain chloroplasts, and may perform various functions besides those of mechanical tissue.

As a rule mechanical tissues are arranged in the plant in what seems to be the most efficient way. A vertical stem needs to have mechanical tissue placed where it will produce stiffness and prevent the stem from being too easily bent over by the wind. Now, when a vertical column is bent over, if it does not break, there must be a stretching on one

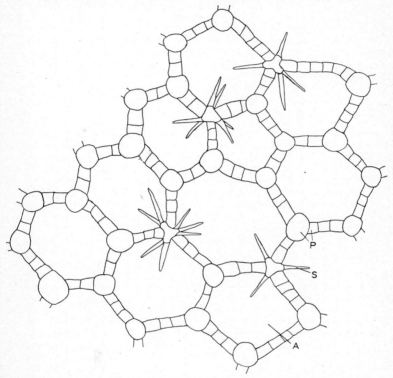

Fig. 9.—Portion of cross-section of water lily petiole showing sclereids. *P*, parenchyma cells; *S*, sclereid; *A*, air space.

side and a compression on the other. Both the compression and the stretching decrease toward the center until they become zero at the center of the column. Mechanical tissue right at the center, therefore, would not produce stiffness and it is a well known fact that mechanical tissue is very seldom found at the center of a stem. The center is filled with pith and the mechanical tissue is near the outside. Furthermore, it is well known to mechanical engineers that the most economical way to construct a column, that is, the way to get maximum strength in proportion to the material used, is to make it hollow but with a wall whose thickness is equal to about one-seventh the total diameter of the column. We find that many herbaceous stems closely conform to this mechanical principle by having the layer of supporting tissue equal in thickness to about one-seventh the diameter of the stem. Stems that are square, like those of many mints, often have most of the mechanical tissue in the angles and this is, of course, the very best place for it (Fig. 10).

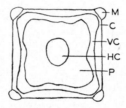

Fig. 10.—Diagram of a mint stem showing mechanical tissue at the angles. *M*, mechanical tissue; *C*, cortex; *VC*, vascular tissue; *HC*, hollow center; *P*, pith.

Roots, on the other hand, do not need to be stiff. They need rather to be able to resist a pull and, since the pull is not always straight, they need to be able to bend without breaking. Accordingly we find that the mechanical tissue of roots is often largely near the center and that there is a thick cortex of thin-walled cells.

As in the case of conducting tissues the chief factor influencing the development of mechanical tissue is water, or rather, lack of water. Many submerged water plants are almost entirely without mechanical tissue. Such plants may entirely collapse as soon as removed from the water. All seed plants that grow out of the water, however, have some mechanical tissue and this tissue reaches its maximum development in plants growing in desert regions.

20. **Protective Tissues.**—The greatest danger to which most land plants are subjected is too great a loss of water. While roots are better protected than most stems by virtue of their position, stems are better protected structurally than any other plant parts except seeds. The most important protective tissues of stems are the epidermis in herbaceous and young woody stems and cork in older stems. The epidermis ordinarily consists of a single layer of cells the outer walls of which are water-proofed by a deposit of cutin, making up what is called the cuticle. Cutin is probably never deposited except on walls that are exposed to the air. The presence of air, however, is most likely an indirect factor, the direct factor being evaporation or desiccation since the cuticle is most strongly developed where there is free exposure in dry situations.

In perennial stems the epidermis usually becomes ruptured during the second or third years and its function is taken over by a complex of tissues commonly called bark. Bark consists largely of phlœm and cork and it is the cork that makes it an efficient protective layer. Cork is a tissue the cell walls of which have been water-proofed by a deposit of suberin. The efficiency of suberin as a water-proofing substance is well known through the use of commercial cork, obtained from the bark of the cork oak, for bottle stoppers and many other purposes. Just as in the development of cuticle, the chief factor in the formation of cork seems to be desiccation. The initial step in cork formation is probably always a cutinization or suberization of walls, usually in the presence of air, which blocks the flow of sap and results in an accumulation of food. This accumulation of food brings about the formation of a growing tissue called a cork cambium which produces the cork tissue.

21. **Stem Habits.**—In plants with foliage the greatest loss of water takes place through the leaves. For this reason

the various habits of growth and of foliage display result in varying degrees of protection from excessive loss of water. From this point of view woody plants may be classified as follows:

(a) *Tropical Evergreen Trees and Shrubs.*—These are the only plants that can be said to have unrestricted foliage display. They grow in the rain forests of the tropics where the uniform climate and ever abundant moisture make protection unnecessary. The conditions for growth in such a place are in many respects ideal and the vegetation is very luxuriant. The stems of the bamboo which grow in these forests are among the most rapid growers known. They sometimes grow nearly a foot in one day. On the other hand the great luxuriance of the vegetation brings about an intense competition for space.

(b) *Sclerophyllous Evergreen Trees and Shrubs.*—Sclerophyllous evergreens are those in which the epidermis of the leaves is composed of thick walled (sclerenchyma) cells with a very heavy cuticle. Such an epidermis makes the leaf stiff and leathery. Sclerophyllous plants are of two general types. In regions having hot dry summers and warm wet winters, as in some parts of southern California, the sclerophyllous vegetation has broad flat leaves. Examples of this type are the holly, the live oak and the olive (Fig. 11). In regions with cold winters, on the other hand, we find sclerophyllous plants with the familiar needle-shaped leaves of the pines and spruces. In either case the advantage of the sclerophyllous habit is that with the protection afforded by the heavy epidermis these plants are able to display their foliage at all times and so to carry on photosynthesis throughout the year. At the same time there is the disadvantage that this type of leaf, which effectually reduces the rate of transpiration, also reduces the rate of gas exchange and so the rate of photosynthesis. The plants, therefore, are never able to manufacture food so rapidly as can the tropical evergreens.

(c) *Leafless Evergreen Trees and Shrubs.*—These plants are still better protected than the sclerophyllous plants because the surface from which water may be lost is so very

Fig. 11.—*Ceanothus cuneatus* near Palo Alto, California. A broad leaf sclerophyll. (Photograph by W. S. Cooper.)

greatly reduced. Since they have no leaves all food manufacture has to be done by the stems and the surface for interchange of gases for this work is also greatly reduced. Such plants cannot manufacture carbohydrates rapidly and so cannot grow rapidly. Examples of leafless evergreen trees are the giant cactus and other large cacti of the American deserts and the large spurges of the African deserts (Fig. 12).

(d) *Deciduous Trees and Shrubs.*—Woody plants that drop their leaves at the beginning of a dry or a cold (physiologically dry) season are said to be deciduous. Such plants, during the favorable seasons are as well fitted for maximum efficiency in food manufacture as are the tropical evergreens, while during the unfavorable seasons, they are better protected than any of the evergreens except, perhaps, some of the leafless ones. These of course are obvious advantages. On the other hand deciduous trees and shrubs are at some disadvantage in that they have to expend a lot of energy in constructing an entirely new set of leaves at the beginning of each growing season, and, also, in that they have absolutely no chance to manufacture any carbohydrates during the unfavorable season even though there may occur some very favorable days.

(e) *Evergreen Herbs.*—There are various sorts of evergreen herbaceous plants. Some, as the winter greens, have sclerophyllous leaves while others, as hepatica and dandelion, have leaves that are not protected by the sclerophyllous structure. There are also some leafless evergreen herbs, such as the prickly pear (*Opuntia*). In all cases these herbs are better protected than the corresponding evergreen trees and shrubs because of their low stature. The leafless herbs can endure full exposure but the majority of those that have leaves grow in places where they receive some protection from fallen leaves of other plants or from a covering of snow.

(f) *Deciduous Herbs.*—These are perennial plants in which all aërial parts die at the beginning of an unfavorable season. In some, as the blood-root (*Sanguinaria canadensis*), only leaves are deciduous but in a greater number there are aërial stems which also die down to the ground each year. In connection with these latter it is proper to speak of stem fall as well as leaf fall. These plants, since they live through the unfavorable season as underground structures, are exceedingly well protected, but they have a considerable amount of construction work to do at the beginning of each growing season and, of course, they cannot display their foliage as efficiently as plants with perennial aërial stems.

FIG. 12.—*Pachycereus Pringlei*, tree cactus, Sonora, Mexico. A leafless evergreen. (Photograph by W. S. Cooper.)

(*g*) *Annual Plants.*—Annual plants are better protected during the unfavorable seasons than any other kinds because they live through those seasons only as seeds. During the growing season, however, these plants are practically without protection, but this is not disadvantageous. The chief disadvantage of the annual habit is the necessity of reconstructing the entire plant each year.

22. **Stems as Storage Organs.**—Stems are nearly as important as storage organs as are roots. One of the most conspicuous structural characteristics of the stems of water plants is the presence of large air spaces where oxygen and carbon dioxide accumulate in considerable quantities. On the other hand, the cacti and many other plants that grow in places that are either physically or physiologically dry are characterized by fleshy stems which accumulate water. Such stems are spoken of as being succulent.

Food accumulates in greater or less quantities in practically all sorts of stems. It is found mostly in the parenchyma tissues of the cortex, medullary rays, pith, and wood. This food consists largely of carbohydrates, chiefly starch. In woody stems, especially, much of the starch is changed to sugar during cold weather so that the amount of sugar increases and the amount of starch decreases as the winter season progresses. Under ground stems obviously have the same advantages as roots as storage organs.

Some families of plants are characterized by the presence of a milky juice called latex. This is usually white though in some cases it is some other color. The latex is entirely different from the sap of the plant and occurs in special latex receptacles. These receptacles differ in different kinds of plants. In the bloodroot and in the convolvulus and soapwort families the latex is found in single enlarged cells called latex sacs. These are usually arranged in longitudinal rows but they are not fused. In some members of the poppy and composite families the latex sacs become fused together either longitudinally only or, especially in the composites, both longitudinally and laterally. Thus a sort of circulatory system of latex vessels is produced. Structures such as these that are formed by the fusion of a number of cells are called syncytes. The mushroom genus *Lactarius* also has latex vessels of the syncyte type. Finally in the spurges and milkweeds the latex vessels are cœnocytes. This means that each latex vessel is composed of several cells which, however, have never been separated from each other by walls so that the vessel seems to be a single large cell with several nuclei. It starts as an ordinary cell in the embryo of the plant. This cell elongates, becomes multinucleate (cœnocytic), branches, and penetrates the tissues of the plant like a parasite until it finally forms a sort of circulatory system extending from one end of the plant to the other.

Very little is known about the function of latex and the probability is that it has no definite function. It is not characteristic of plants that grow in any particular kind of environment. While a majority of plants with latex are found in dry climates, many occur where the water supply is adequate and some even grow in the wet rain forests of the tropics. It does not appear, therefore, that the latex is of any particular advantage. There is usually found in the latex some of practically everything that is produced in the plant, including foods of various kinds and waste materials. This indicates that the latex receptacles are in a sense catch-all reservoirs into which anything that is produced in excess of demand may be dumped. In some species of spurge very interesting rod-shaped or soup-bone-shaped starch grains are found in the latex receptacles.

23. Variations in Stem Form.—The stems of different kinds of plants vary very greatly in shape and size. All gradations are found from a small fraction of an inch to 20 or more feet in diameter and from less than 1 inch to 300 or more feet in length. These differences are to a large extent inherited. There occur also very great variations in the stems of individuals of the same species which are due to the external factors of the environment. A sugar maple tree growing alone in the open usually has a relatively short main stem with numerous large branches well down toward the base while an individual of the same species growing in a dense forest has a long trunk with no branches on the lower half (Fig. 13). The same statement is true of most species of

4

trees and a similar statement would be true of many herbaceous plants.

The two factors that seem most likely as causes of these
stem variations are light and moisture. Light has usually
been regarded as having a retarding effect upon growth,
and especially upon elongation, while absence of light favors
elongation. Recent work has cast considerable doubt upon

Fig. 13.—Sugar maple forest showing long trunks with the first branches
far from the base.

this general statement concerning light and in any case it is
certain that light has often been over-emphasized as a factor
affecting the elongation of stems.

Moisture is much more important in this respect. Nearly
all seed plants absorb water through their roots and lose
water by transpiration from their leaves and stems. In
general there must be a balance between these two processes

and the height to which any plant can grow is limited by the height to which it can transport water rapidly enough to counterbalance the loss by transpiration. This fact is strikingly shown by certain water plants with floating leaves in which the conducting system is ordinarily poorly developed. There is, of course, no transpiration below the surface of the water but above the surface transpiration is rapid. The length of the stems of these water plants is thus governed by the depth of the water and very great variations in the same species are sometimes found.

Somewhat comparable to the variation in stem length in water is the elongation of certain kinds of stems that are being gradually buried by the sand of a moving sand-dune. Some woody plants, such as willows, poplars and dogwoods, grow very rapidly as the sand piles up around them and the stems may become several times as long as normally. Such plants, however, produce adventitious roots from the stem in the sand so that the distance from the top of the plant to the nearest roots, and thus to the water supply, is never excessive.

The dwarfing of plants is likewise to be explained largely on the basis of a balance between absorption and transpiration. All desert plants are more or less dwarf, that is, none of them grow very tall, but the most typical dwarf plants are found in Arctic and Alpine regions. In such places the low temperature of the soil makes absorption slow and difficult while the strong, dry winds tend to increase the transpiration rate. The result is that some plants which under more favorable conditions might develop into tall trees never become more than a few inches high although they may live for several hundred years. In many Arctic and Alpine regions the height of the woody plants is controlled largely by the depth of the snow. They grow upward as far as they can during the favorable season but during the winter all parts that project above the snow, and so are unprotected, are killed through desiccation (Fig. 14).

Tubers, such as those of the potato and many other plants, are very much shortened and thickened stems and are, therefore, somewhat comparable to dwarf stems. The causes of tuber formation are not well understood. Although tubers are most abundant in dry regions yet many tuber-producing plants grow where there is an abundance of water so that desiccation cannot be the only cause of tuber

Fig. 14.—Engleman spruce dwarfed at timber line and showing upright branches killed during the winter.

formation, and, until a great deal more experimental work has been done, it is not possible to go beyond the unsatisfactory statement that the production of tubers is an inherited characteristic of the plants on which they are produced.

REFERENCES.

Cooper, William S.: The Broad Sclerophyll Vegetation of California, Carnegie Inst. Publ., 1922, **319**, 124, 43 fig., 21 pl.

Coulter, J. M., Barnes, C. E. and Cowles, H. C.: A Text-book of Botany. Vol. II. Ecology. Chapter III, Stems. American Book Company, 1911.

Hayden, Ada: The Ecologic Subterranian Anatomy of Some Plants of a Prairie Province in Central Iowa, Am. Jour. Bot. 1919, **6**, 87–106.

McDougall, W. B. and Penfound, W. T.: Ecological Anatomy of Some Deciduous Forest Plants, Ecology, 1928, **9**, 349–353.

Priestley, J. H. and Woffenden, Lettice M.: Physiological Studies in Plant Anatomy. V. Causal Factors in Cork Formation, New Phytol., 1922, **21**, 252–268.

CHAPTER IV.

THE ECOLOGY OF LEAVES.

The principal function of leaves is food manufacture. Many leaves are modified to perform other special functions and in some plants stems are more important than leaves as food manufacturing organs. In some cases, furthermore, leaves are reduced to mere scales and perform no function at all. As a general rule the greatest danger to which leaves are subjected is excessive transpiration and for this reason the structure of the leaves is in a sense a compromise between what would be best as a photosynthetic organ and what is necessary to safeguard against too rapid a loss of water.

24. **Structure and Arrangement of Tissues.**—The tissues of the leaf that vary most with variations in the environment are those that contain chlorophyll. Variations in the fibro-vascular bundles and their sheaths, so far as our present knowledge of them goes, do not seem to be of much ecological significance.

The majority of plants that grow in exposed places where there is an adequate supply of water have leaves with no chlorophyll in the epidermis except in the guard cells of the stomata, but with chlorophyll in all other cells except those of the fibro-vascular bundles and their sheaths. The tissues that contain chlorophyll are called collectively, chlorenchyma. In the typical leaf of which we are speaking the upper half of the chlorenchyma is made up of elongated cells with their long axes perpendicular to the epidermis. These cells because of their shape are called palisade cells. The lower half of the chlorenchyma, on the other hand, is made up of irregularly-shaped parenchyma cells and has

(53)

numerous intercellular spaces.   For this reason it is called
spongy parenchyma (Fig. 15).

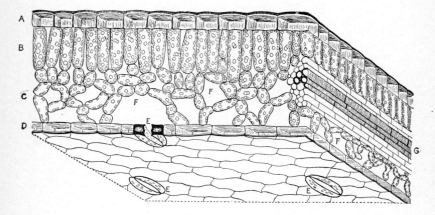

Fig. 15.—Sectional and surface views of an ordinary leaf.   A, upper
epidermis; B, palisade layer; C, spongy layer; D, lower epidermis; E, stoma;
F, air space; G, vein.   (From Sinnott's Botany—Principles and Problems,
New York, McGraw-Hill Book Company, Inc.)

If now we examine the leaves of plants growing in progressively wetter places we shall find a progressive decrease in
the amount of palisade tissue and a progressive increase in
spongy parenchyma until in the case of leaves which are
submerged in water there is no palisade tissue at all, the
chlorenchyma being made up entirely of spongy parenchyma with very large intercellular spaces (Fig. 16).   The
leaves of plants that grow in wet places, and especially in
dense shade, often have chlorophyll in the epidermal cells
and for this reason are dark green in color.

On the other hand if we examine the leaves of plants
growing in progressively drier places we shall find that there
is a progressive decrease in the amount of spongy parenchyma
and a progressive increase in the amount of palisade tissue
until in the case of plants growing in very dry places there is

no spongy parenchyma at all and the chlorenchyma may consist entirely of palisade tissue (Fig. 17). There are, of

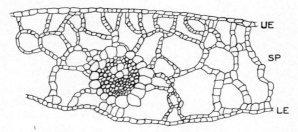

FIG. 16.—Section of a leaf of a water plant, pondweed (*Potamogeton*).
UE, upper epidermis; *SP*, spongy tissue; *LE*, lower epidermis.

course, many exceptions to these general conditions, especially in dry regions where very great variations in leaf structure occur.

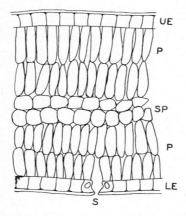

FIG. 17.—Section of a leaf of a desert plant, mesquite (*Prosopis velutina*).
UE, upper epidermis; *P*, palisade tissue; *SP*, spongy tissue; *LE*, lower epidermis; *S*, stoma.

There are three general types of these exceptions that are sufficiently common to be worthy of mention here, although this by no means exhausts the list. One of these is a leaf in which there is palisade both above and below with some spongy parenchyma between. This is most likely to be found in leaves that have a vertical or nearly vertical orientation so that the two sides of each leaf are about equally exposed. A second type is that found in plants with succulent, or fleshy, leaves. In these the chlorenchyma is often reduced to a few layers of cells and the larger part of the leaf tissue is made up of colorless water storage cells. This tissue is sometimes next the epidermis and in other cases occupies the central portion of the leaf. A convenient term that is often used to designate all of the internal tissues of a leaf, with the exception of the veins, is mesophyll. Thus in a succulent leaf the mesophyll is partly chlorenchyma and partly water storage tissue. In Arctic regions and at high elevations on mountains there is a third common type of leaf in which the mesophyll is made up entirely of chlorenchyma which can be said to be neither palisade nor spongy tissue. Rather it is a very compact parenchyma tissue of rounded or angular cells.

25. The Causes of Palisade Development.—The two factors that have usually been thought to have most influence on palisade development are light and transpiration. The amount of palisade tissue often varies considerably according to the relative exposure of the plant. A plant of wild lettuce (*Lactuca scariola*), for example, which has grown in a fully exposed place has relatively thick leaves, the mesophyll of which is all palisade tissue, while a plant of the same species, which has grown in deep shade, may have leaves only a third as thick as the former plant and with scarcely any palisade tissue. These different types of leaves from the same species are spoken of as sun leaves and shade leaves respectively. In the case of trees, such as the maple, it is often possible to collect leaves from the same individual plant which have the structural characteristics of typical sun and shade leaves; the sun leaves being taken from the south side of the tree where they are fully exposed to light and the shade leaves from the north side of the tree near the base where they are protected from the sun during practically the whole day.

The fact that palisade tissue is best developed in leaves that are fully exposed to the sun has led to the belief that the significance of the palisade shape of cells is concerned with the protection of the chloroplasts from intense light rays. Although chlorophyll is produced only in light and must have light in order to function, yet light that is too intense destroys chlorophyll by causing its disintegration. In a leaf that has been exposed to direct sunlight for some time the majority of the chloroplasts are found to be arranged along the walls that are perpendicular to the surface where they have a measure of protection from the direct rays of light. On the other hand, a leaf from the same species, but which has been for some time in diffuse light, usually shows many chloroplasts along the walls that are parallel to the surface where they may receive a maximum amount of the incident light. A similar response to varying intensities of light is seen in the alga, *Mougeotia*, in which there is a single rectangular, plate-like chloroplast in each cell. While this plant is in diffuse light the chloroplast of each cell ordinarily presents its broad side to the direction of the incident light but when the plant is placed in direct sunlight the chloroplast makes a half turn so that its edge is toward the light.

Although the evidence is strong that light is a factor in the development of palisade tissue yet its influence in this respect has probably often been over-emphasized. When a plant is fully exposed to light it is also exposed to rapid transpiration. It has already been shown that palisade development reaches its maximum in dry land plants where transpiration, in proportion to the rate of absorption, is most rapid. The probability that transpiration is the principal cause of palisade development is also shown by many water plants that have both submerged and aërial leaves. In these cases there is an abrupt change in the degree of palisade development at the surface of the water, the aërial leaves having much palisade tissue and the submerged leaves none. The change in light intensity here is, of course, not abrupt while the change in transpiration rate is. Here, therefore, as in so many other cases, water appears to be the most important factor.

26. **Structure as a Basis for Classifying Leaves.**—Broad leaves, as opposed to needle-shaped leaves and reduced or scale-like leaves, are often classified into four groups on the basis of the structural differences discussed in paragraph 24. Leaves which have palisade tissue toward the upper side and spongy tissue toward the lower side, so that the two sides of the leaf are very different in their photosynthetic and other relations, are called diphotophylls (Fig. 15). Those that have palisade tissue on both sides with spongy tissue between, so that the two sides of the leaf are essentially the same, are called diplophylls, meaning double leaves (Fig. 17). The term spongophyll is used for a leaf having spongy parenchyma all the way through (Fig. 16), while leaves that have compact tissue all the way through, whether it is composed of palisade cells or not, are called staurophylls.

27. **Air Spaces and Stomata.**—Gaseous exchange between leaves and the atmosphere takes place in connection with three physiological processes: respiration, photosynthesis and transpiration. By far the greatest volume of gas (water vapor) is involved in transpiration and by far the smallest volume in respiration, while photosynthesis is intermediate in this respect. This interchange of gases is rendered possible through the presence of stomata in the epidermis and intercellular air spaces within the leaf. There is usually a comparatively large air chamber beneath each stoma and this leads into intercellular spaces of varying sizes that form a connected system of passageways throughout the interior of the leaf. The cell walls that are adjacent to these passages and chambers are thin and are always wet, and the gases diffuse inward and outward through the pro-

toplasmic membranes of the cells while in solution in the water.

The primary cause of the development of air spaces is probably just the opposite of that causing the development of palisade tissue, that is, lack of transpiration. Air spaces are always numerous and comparatively large in the spongy tissue of diphotophylls and they reach their highest development in submerged spongophylls and in the stems and petioles of submerged water plants. On the other hand, air spaces are small and inconspicuous in palisade tissue and are least developed in the staurophylls and succulent leaves of plants of dry and cold regions.

In submerged water plants the air spaces often exceed the tissues themselves in volume. In some cases they are undoubtedly of considerable importance as gas reservoirs. Oxygen is commonly present in abundance in ordinary lakes, ponds and streams but in swamps and other stagnant bodies of water it is present only in very limited amounts. For this reason, if there were not a supplementary supply to draw upon, the plants often would have difficulty in getting enough of this gas for respiration. But the oxygen that is liberated in photosynthesis during the day accumulates in the air spaces and is available for respiration during the night as well as in the day time. Carbon dioxide is usually present in water in abundance so that its accumulation in the air reservoirs for purposes of photosynthesis is probably never really needed.

In some cases, also, the air spaces serve the function of giving buoyancy to the plant or plant part. For example the winter buds of such plants as the duckweeds and the bladderworts, when they are first formed during summer and autumn, are lacking in air spaces of any considerable size. They are heavier than water and in autumn they break off from the parent plants and sink to the bottom. In spring large air spaces develop in the buds and when these become filled with gases they cause the buds to rise to the surface of the water where they develop into mature plants. Water hyacinth (*Eichhornia*) plants are caused to float and to hold their leaves just above the surface of the water by the large air spaces in an enlarged portion of each petiole. A somewhat similar function is performed in the case of some filamentous algæ, such as *Spirogyra*, by the bubbles of oxygen that become entangled in the mass of filaments. A rain storm will wash out this oxygen and cause the plants to sink to the bottom but with the return of sunlight photosynthesis begins and the oxygen that is liberated soon causes the plants to rise again to the surface. This phenomenon is of considerable advantage to these plants since it brings them into a more favorable position with respect to light and to the necessary gases as well.

28. **Structure and Arrangement of Stomata.**—A stoma is a small slit-like opening through the epidermis (Fig. 18). It occurs between two modified epidermal cells, called guard cells, which, in surface view, appear kidney-shaped and have their ends in contact. In cross-section the guard cells are seen to vary considerably in different kinds of plants. They are usually smaller than the other epidermal cells and in some cases the walls are uniformly thickened while in others they are unevenly thickened. In some guard cells the walls next the aperture are thicker than those on the opposite sides of the cells, while in others the outer and inner walls are thick and the lateral walls thinner. Many other modifications are found although the general structural features are practically the same for all stomata.

Most stomata have some capacity for opening and closing. This is done automatically by the increase or decrease of the turgidity of the guard cells. An increase in turgidity causes the cells to expand in the direction perpendicular to the surface. This straightens somewhat the walls that bulge out to form the aperture and so opens up the stoma. As the cells dry out the turgidity decreases, the cells collapse somewhat, and the walls that form the aperture come nearly or

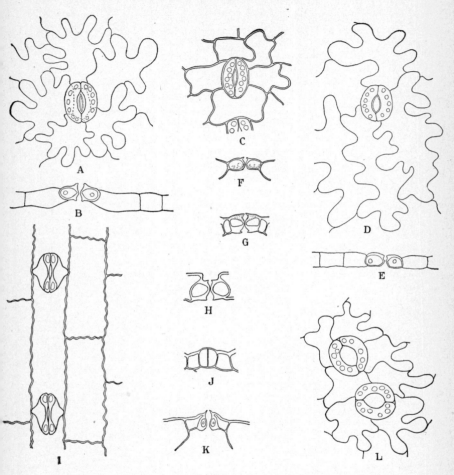

Fig. 18.—Stomata. *A, B,* from *Solanum tuberosum,* in face view and cross section; *C,* from *Pyrus malus; D, E,* from *Lactuca sativa; F,* from *Medeola virginica; G,* from *Aplectrum hyemale; H,* from *Polygonatum biflorum; I, J, K,* from *Zea Mays: I,* face view; *J,* cross section through end of stoma; *K,* median cross-section; *L,* from *Cucumis sativus* (*F, G, H,* and *J,* after Copeland). (From Eames and McDaniels—Introduction to Plant Anatomy, New York, McGraw-Hill Book Company, Inc.)

quite together, thus closing the stoma and greatly reducing the amount of water that may be given off by transpiration.

The arrangement of the stomata seems to be largely a matter of inheritance rather than environment. In the majority of monocotyledonous plants the stomata are arranged on the leaves in more or less definite rows and have their long axes extending lengthwise of the leaves. This is true also of some dicotyledonous plants that have long narrow leaves. In most dicotyledonous plants, however, the stomata are scattered irregularly and have their long axes extending in various directions.

The question as to whether stomata shall develop at all, however, is, to a certain extent at least, a matter of environment. The majority of plants that have their leaves fully exposed to the sun have stomata on the lower surfaces of their leaves only. This is true of most trees and many herbaceous plants although there are exceptions. Most grasses that grow in exposed places, for instance, have stomata only on the upper surface, but this is the surface that is most protected in dry weather when the leaves of these plants roll. Plants that grow in the shade, on the other hand, usually have stomata on both surfaces. In water plants, leaves that are submersed are without stomata while leaves of the same plant that are above the water may have stomata on both sides. Floating leaves commonly have stomata on the upper surface only.

29. **Protection from Excessive Transpiration.**—It used to be said frequently that transpiration is a necessary evil. Certainly excessive transpiration is the greatest danger to which most plants are subjected. Its necessity has been considered as due to the fact that there must be openings for the interchange of gases in order that respiration and photosynthesis may be carried on and if there are openings of any sort it is not possible to entirely prevent transpiration. In other words, it would be a simple matter to construct a leaf that would not allow any transpiration but such a leaf would be

useless as a photosynthetic organ. It is now believed, however, that transpiration is not entirely an evil but is often of considerable importance to the plant because of its cooling effect. It takes a considerable amount of heat to evaporate water and, just as evaporation of water from a canvas water-bag keeps the water inside the bag cool, so transpiration from a leaf prevents the internal temperature from going so high as to prove disastrous to the protoplasm. This is, of course, especially true of leaves that are exposed to the full light and heat of the sun since a great deal of radiant energy is absorbed under such conditions. In spite of the obvious necessity of transpiration, however, the presence of an adequate amount of water within the plant is so vital that the possibility of losing it faster than it can be absorbed is an ever present and very real danger. For this reason we find a variety of structural modifications that appear to be designed to prevent excessive transpiration.

The stomatal movements described in paragraph 28 tend to control the rate of transpiration. In many cases, also, the stomata themselves are protected in one way or another. Sometimes they are merely sunken below the level of the epidermis, which protects them from air currents. Sometimes, as in the oleander, several stomata are grouped within a pocket-like depression which is clothed with hairs. Again, they may have extra well developed outer and inner vestibules, or a labyrinthiform passageway in place of the simple slit. Any of these devices tend to retard the exit of water.

In practically all leaves that are exposed to the air the epidermis itself is covered with a layer of cutin which renders it so nearly water-proof that transpiration is confined almost entirely to the stomata. Sometimes the cutin is reinforced, or in some cases replaced, by a coating of wax or of resin. This not only retards transpiration directly but also tends to check rapid heating of the leaf, which in turn influences the rate of transpiration. In the case of floating leaves, such as those of the water lily, the waxy covering has another use in that it prevents the surface from becoming wet. This facilitates the interchange of gases for respiration and photosynthesis by preventing the stomata from becoming clogged with water.

The surfaces of many leaves, as well as stems and other plant parts, are often covered with hairs. These may be simple or branched. Usually the simple hairs stand perpendicular to the surface but in a few cases, as on the bud scales of Norway maple, they are closely appressed, or, in other cases, as on the stems of Florida moss (*Tillandsia*), they are scale-like and overlap like the shingles of a roof. The common mullein (*Verbascum thapsus*) has multicellular hairs that are much branched and form a woolly covering of the leaves. These various kinds of hairs have been thought to be rather efficient organs of protection against excessive transpiration. In many cases they doubtless do afford some protection, especially in windy weather, but recent experiments and observations seem to indicate that their efficiency in this respect has often been over-emphasized.

One of the most efficient means of protection against excessive loss of water is by reducing the transpiration surface. Most efficient of all, perhaps, is the periodic reduction brought about by leaf fall which will be discussed in paragraph 30. Many plants, however, have a permanently reduced transpiration surface. The extreme condition is represented by leafless plants in which the photosynthetic function is performed by stems. Among plants with leaves there are all variations from water plants with leaves that are only one or two cells thick to plants which have leaves that are freely exposed and which are round in cross-section and so have a minimum of surface in proportion to volume. Of course any reduction in transpiration surface reduces also the photosynthetic surface but the condition of each plant represents a compromise between two major needs—one for free gaseous exchange for photosynthesis and the other for protection from excessive loss of water.

Some plants, especially members of the legume family, exhibit interesting leaf movements commonly called sleep movements. These consist of a closing up of the compound leaves during the night or sometimes during the hottest part of the day in time of drought. The leaves of the sensitive plant (*Mimosa*) not only close during the night but they close quickly whenever anything comes in contact with them. This movement is brought about by a mechanism at the base of the petiole (and also at the base of each leaflet) called the pulvinus. The decrease in turgidity of the cells in the pulvinus as the water suddenly passes from them into the adjoining intercellular spaces causes the leaves to close. They slowly resume their former position when the water reënters the cells. In some cases, as in bean leaves, the closing is due to an increase of turgidity which is greater on one side of the pulvinus than on the other. No satisfactory explanation of the causes of these increases and decreases of turgidity has yet been made. The closing of leaves during drought reduces the exposed surface and probably aids in checking water loss. The more common cases of night closing, however, and the sudden movements of Mimosa leaves are probably of no real benefit to the plants.

30. **Leaf Fall.**—A deciduous tree is one that drops all of its leaves at the beginning of a cold or a dry season. Contrasted with these are the evergreen trees which drop their leaves only after a new crop has been produced and so always have some green leaves. In any case the fall of the leaf is brought about directly by the formation of a special separation layer, called the absciss layer, at the base of the petiole. The absciss layer consisting of two or more thicknesses of very thin-walled cells is formed during the development of the leaf. At the time of leaf fall the walls of these cells become softened and finally disintegrate. A gentle wind or the weight of a film of dew is then enough to cause the leaf to fall. In some trees, especially in some of the oaks,

5

the absciss layer is very imperfectly formed and the leaves therefore hang on during the greater part of the winter. On the other hand, in some compound leaves an absciss layer forms first at the base of each leaflet and these drop off. Later the petioles also drop.

The cause of the formation of an absciss layer is not known. In regions with periodical dry seasons it is probably largely desiccation brought about by increased transpiration without any increase in rate of absorption. In regions with cold seasons, too, the cause may be desiccation since, for plants, a cold season is a dry season, that is, it is a season when transpiration continues but absorption is very greatly reduced because of the low temperature of the soil. Contrary to a rather common belief frost does not ordinarily cause leaf fall. In fact an early frost may delay leaf fall by interfering with the development of the absciss layer.

31. **The Forms of Leaves.**—Leaf form is to a large extent a matter of inheritance. So true is this that very many species of plants are easily identified by their leaves alone. To be sure there may be considerable variation in the leaves of an individual plant. The first leaves, or cotyledons, are always very different from the later ones. In the garden bean the second pair of leaves as well as the cotyledons are simple while the later ones are compound. A single mulberry tree may show all variations from an unlobed leaf to one that is very much lobed. The leaves of a single plant may also vary as much as 100 per cent or more in size. But with all this variation a mulberry leaf never looks like an elm leaf. Inheritance is too potent a factor for that.

Nevertheless, there are some variations of leaf form that are more or less characteristic of certain types of environment. Plants that grow where there is an adequate supply of water have relatively thin and broad leaves, while plants growing where there is difficulty in getting sufficient water have smaller and thicker leaves. Furthermore, it has been shown by experiment in the case of many species that the same individual will develop larger and thinner leaves when grown in a moist environment than when grown in a dry environment. These facts seem to indicate that here again water, perhaps transpiration, is a very influential factor, though probably it is not the only one.

The influence of water on leaf form is brought out even more strikingly in the case of many water plants. In some of these, such as the mermaid weed (*Proserpinaca palustris*) and lake cress (*Radicula aquatica*), the aërial leaves, which are subjected to transpiration, are nearly or quite entire, while the leaves that are in the water are very much lobed or finely dissected. The water fern (*Salvinia natans*) has broad floating leaves that do the work of photosynthesis and very much dissected leaves that hang down into the water like roots and serve as absorbing organs. In these cases there can be no question of the influence of water on the form of the leaves.

32. **Leaves as Storage Organs.**—Food storage in leaves is usually only temporary. Permanent storage of food in these organs would seriously interfere with their photosynthetic function. Food usually accumulates in the leaves while it is being manufactured during the day because it is synthesized more rapidly than it can be transported to other parts of the plant. The transportation continues during the night, however, so that by morning the leaf is ordinarily without stored food.

Nevertheless, there are some plants whose leaves are the chief organs for permanent food storage. The century plant, which is a species of *Agave*, is a well-known example of such a plant. This plant grows vegetatively for from six to fifteen or twenty years, storing up food and water in its large, succulent leaves. It then sends up a flowering shoot which grows very rapidly and upon which a large number of flowers and fruits develop and mature. By the time this has been accomplished, the leaves have been drained of their stored materials and the plant dies.

Water accumulation in leaves, however, is often of considerable importance. This is especially true of plants with fleshy or succulent leaves (Fig. 19). Such plants are characteristic of some desert regions and of salt marshes and other saline areas where, because of the high concentration of the soil solution, absorption of water is difficult. The retention of water by succulent leaves, which in some cases is remarkably efficient, is accomplished by one or the other of

Fig. 19.—*Agave applanata.* LaMortola, Mexico. A plant with succulent leaves. (Photograph by William Trelease. Courtesy of Dr. George T. Moore and the Missouri Botanical Garden.)

two general methods. The first of these is by strong cutinization, layers of wax, or other modifications of the epidermis. The other method consists in maintaining a very high concentration of the cell sap, which effectively reduces the evapporation rate. Some succulent leaves when removed from the plant and freely exposed do not become entirely dry for weeks.

Crystals of calcium oxalate and sometimes of calcium carbonate, are often stored in leaves as well as in stems.

These are to be regarded as waste materials. Since a plant has no regular excretory organs it is sometimes necessary to store up certain products of metabolism in the form of insoluble crystals in order to get them out of solution. The leaf would seem to be a good place to store such crystals because when the leaf falls the crystals are gotten rid of. Crystals stored in the cortex or bark of a perennial stem are also disposed of eventually as the bark sloughs off from the outside.

REFERENCES.

Coulter, J. M., Barnes, C. E. and Cowles, H. C.: A Text-book of Botany. Vol. II. Ecology. Chapter II. Leaves, American Book Company, 1911.

Clements, E. S.: Relation of Leaf Structure to Physical Factors, Trans. Am. Micro. Soc., 1904, **26**, 19–102, Pl. 1–9.

Hanson, Herbert C.: Leaf-structure as Related to Environment, Am. Jour. Bot., 1917, **4**, 533–560, Fig. 1–21.

Harshberger, John W.: The Vegetation of the New Jersey Pine Barrens. Chapter XVIII, Leaf Forms of Pine Barren Plants and Chapter XIX, Microscopic Leaf Structure, Christopher Sower Co., Philadelphia, 1916.

Hayden, Ada: The Ecologic Foliar Anatomy of Some Plants of a Prairie Province in Central Iowa, Am. Jour. Bot., 1919, **6**, 69–85.

Starr, Anna M.: Comparative Anatomy of Dune Plants, Bot. Gaz., 1912, **54**, 265–306.

Stober, J. P.: A Comparative Study of Winter and Summer Leaves of Various Herbs, Bot. Gaz., 1917, **63**, 89–109.

CHAPTER V.

SYMBIOSIS—DISJUNCTIVE.

SYMBIOSIS means the living together of two or more unlike organisms, that is, organisms belonging to more than one species. It includes all such cases. While this is a broader definition than has been used by many authors it is the only one that is at all satisfactory. Any attempt to limit the definition of symbiosis leads one into the difficulty of trying to recognize lines of division between living phenomena where no lines exist. Hence it is much better to accept the definition as including all cases of the living together of two or more organisms of different species.

33. **The Classification of Symbiotic Phenomena.**—The various kinds of phenomena included under the term symbiosis are conveniently classified as follows:

I. Disjunctive symbiosis. II. Conjunctive symbiosis
  1. Social   1. Social
  2. Nutritive   2. Nutritive
    (a) Antagonistic   (a) Antagonistic
    (b) Reciprocal   (b) Reciprocal

In disjunctive symbiosis the organisms concerned are not in actual contact, at least not all of the time, while in conjunctive symbiosis the symbionts are in actual contact throughout the time during which they are said to be in a state of symbiosis. Social symbiosis, whether disjunctive or conjunctive, includes all cases in which dissimilar organisms are living together but without any direct food relation; that is, none of the symbionts derive food directly from the others. In nutritive symbiosis, on the other hand, one or more of the symbionts derives food directly from one or more of the other symbionts. Again, when only one or more but not all of the symbionts derive food from other symbionts, and these latter are in no way benefited but often injured by the relationship, the condition is said to be one of antagonistic nutritive symbiosis, but, when all of the organisms concerned obtain food or some other obvious benefit from the relation-

Fig. 20.—A forest community with numerous kinds of plants living together in social disjunctive symbiosis.

ship, they are living in reciprocal nutritive symbiosis, either disjunctive or conjunctive. Examples of these various types of symbiosis will be discussed in succeeding paragraphs.

34. **Social Disjunctive Symbiosis.**—This is the type of symbiosis in which the organisms concerned are not in actual contact, at least not all of the time, and in which there is no direct food relation. It includes, therefore, all of the ordinary interrelations of the various species of plants that are living together in any plant community, such as a forest, a swamp, or a meadow (Fig. 20). Since synecology is concerned almost entirely with these various kinds of plant communities they

will constitute the subject matter of several later chapters and it will suffice here to point out only a few of the social relations concerned. In a forest community, for example, the trees have very important symbiotic relations with all other plants in the forest. This comes about largely through the fact that the trees control to a large extent such factors of the environment as light, space relations, water supply, and to a certain extent available food materials. Through this large measure of control of the environment they even determine what species of plants may live in the forest. The social relations in such a community are in certain respects comparable to those of a human community where man controls the environment. There is usually a well-marked division of labor among the individuals of a human community, some being engaged in supplying food, others in supplying clothing or fuel, others in administering the law, etc. In the plant community there is a somewhat comparable division of labor among the various species, though not among the individuals of the same species. The function in the community of all individuals of the same species is the same, but some species have the function of manufacturing food, some of supplying a ground cover to check evaporation of water from the soil, some to act as scavengers in getting rid of dead bodies, (Fig. 21), etc. One important difference between the human community and the plant community, however, must be kept in mind. In the human community there are ordinarily more or less definitely organized activities carried on for the good of the community as a whole. In the plant community, on the other hand, there is no altruism. It is a case of every plant for itself. The activities of certain species do result advantageously for the community as a whole, but this is due to chance circumstances, and the activities would be carried on just as vigorously if they were resulting in harm to the community. This fundamental difference between the two communities, however, is the natural result of the presence of consciousness in the human species and the lack of it in plants, and as soon as we leave that fact out of consideration the two types of communities become strikingly similar.

Species in a plant community that are very different are often incidentally of very great service to one another. The trees, for example, furnish the shade necessary for some of the herbaceous plants and fungi, while the herbaceous plants furnish a living soil cover which at times prevents undue loss of the soil water which is needed in great quantities by the trees. The trees, likewise, as well as the shrubs, especially

Fig. 21.—*Polyporus giganteus* hastening the decay of a stump.

those near the border of the woods, serve as a windbrake which protects many smaller plants from the danger of too high transpiration rates.

The phenomenon of leaf fall, discussed in the preceding chapter, is of very great importance from the view-point of social disjunctive symbiosis since the fallen leaves form an efficient cover throughout the winter, thus greatly reducing evaporation from herbaceous perennial plants as well as from the surface of the soil. Closely connected with leaf fall, too, are the activities that bring about the decay of the fallen leaves. These are due mostly to bacteria and fungi. These bacteria and fungi are regular members of the community and are living in social disjunctive symbiosis with the higher plants. They are able to live in the community only as a result of the presence of the higher plants, and they render a distinct service to the community by preventing the accumulation of dead bodies.

FIG. 22.—An example of antagonistic nutritive disjunctive symbiosis.

35. **Antagonistic Nutritive Disjunctive Symbiosis.**—In this type of disjunctive symbiosis one or more, but not all, of the organisms concerned receive food from the other symbionts. A familiar example is the relationship between a cow and the grass upon which she feeds (Fig. 22). In exactly the same category, of course, is the interrelation between a herd of bison and the prairie grasses upon which the bison feed, and a similar remark might be made about any species of herbivorous animals.

The interrelations between man and the plants that he cultivates for food are quite comparable to those between herbivorous animals and plants. These, therefore, also represent cases of antagonistic nutritive disjunctive symbiosis. Innumerable examples of this type of symbiosis between insects and plants might be cited. Only a few of the more interesting of these will be discussed in the remaining paragraphs of this chapter.

36. **Leaf-cutting Ants and Fungi.**—Sometimes when one is walking through a tropical forest he may chance to see a green line across the path in front of him. On stopping to observe the line he sees that it is in motion, and a closer inspection shows it to be composed of a large number of ants each carrying over its back a green piece of leaf. These are leaf-cutting ants, often called umbrella ants because of their way of carrying the pieces of leaves over their backs. They have cut the pieces of leaves from some plant, probably a shrub, and are taking them to their nest. Often they entirely strip a shrub of its leaves within a few minutes. They will chew the pieces of leaves into a pulp and spread out the pulp on an area previously cleaned for the purpose. On this leaf pulp the ants plant the mycelium (or spawn) of a mushroom. The workers now take constant care of their mushroom garden, weeding out undesirable fungi, and producing, therefore, almost a pure culture of the fungus that was planted.

The fungus that is grown by the leaf-cutting ants is *Rozites gongylophora,* a toadstool-shaped mushroom. The ants, however, do not permit the plant to produce mushrooms, which are its fruits. Cultivation for many generations, perhaps for centuries, has caused this fungus to produce abnormal vegetative structures just as many of the plants cultivated by man do. These abnormal structures consist of club-like, upward-projecting outgrowths of the mycelium and are called kohlrabies because their abnormal nature makes them comparable to the garden vegetable of the same name. The kohlrabies serve as food for the ants. This cultivation of mushrooms by ants is entirely comparable to the cultivation of vegetables by man and like the latter is an example of antagonistic nutritive disjunctive symbiosis.

37. **Termites and Ambrosia Beetles as Symbionts.**—Termites, commonly called white ants, cultivate fungi in a way com-

parable to that practiced by leaf-cutting ants.   The termites, however, cultivate their fungi on excreta instead of leaf pulp.   Several kinds of fungi have been identified from termite nests; species of *Xylaria, Collybia, Entoloma,* etc.   The termites feed on the mycelium.

Still another somewhat similar symbiotic relationship is that between ambrosia beetles and fungi.   The ambrosia beetles are wood-boring beetles as distinguished from bark-boring beetles.   They bore tunnels into the wood, sometimes rather simple and sometimes much branched.   In these tunnels they plant the mycelium of a fungus.   The fungi cultivated by the ambrosia beetles are not yet known but they probably are some of the lower fungi rather than mushrooms.   The beetles feed upon the mycelium, which often grows so luxuriantly that it completely clogs up the tunnels, and beetles have been known to become imprisoned and to suffer death as a penalty for not being able to eat fast enough to gain an exit through their food supply.

38. **Insectivorous Plants.**—In all of the examples of antagonistic symbiosis so far discussed animal symbionts obtain food from plants.   This condition is just reversed, however, in the case of a limited number of plants which have the power of digesting and absorbing animal food.   These plants are called insectivorous or carnivorous plants.   The best understood perhaps of these insectivorous plants is the sundew (*Drosera*).   Several species of sundew are common in the bogs of the northern United States and Canada. *Drosera rotundifolia,* the commonest species, is a small plant with a rosette of radical leaves.   In summer it sends up a stalk about 6 inches long which bears from one to two dozen small white flowers.   The leaves are rounded or oval in shape, about a centimeter broad, and with hairy petioles of 2 to 5 cm. in length.

The leaves of *Drosera,* which are attractively red in color, are beset on the upper surface with glandular hairs which are rather short at the center of the leaf but progressively longer toward the outside. Each hair has on its knob-like end a sticky drop of semi-liquid substance which glistens in the sun like dew, thus giving the name, sundew, to the plant. When an insect, either by chance or attracted by the brilliancy of color or by the sweetish secretion, comes in contact with any of the hairs it sticks fast. The other hairs of the leaf now begin to bend inward toward the insect until a considerable number of them are in contact with it. The presence of the insect not only stimulates the hairs to bend inward but also to secrete protein-digesting enzymes. The digestible portions of the insect are thus rendered soluble and are absorbed by the leaf as food. After the insect has been digested the secretion of enzymes ceases, the hairs slowly bend back to their former positions, and the leaf is ready for the next victim. It is interesting to note that inorganic bodies, such as particles of sand, or anything not containing proteins, do not stimulate the hairs to secrete enzymes or to move in any way.

Quite comparable to the sundews so far as symbiosis is concerned, although belonging to a different family of plants, are the butterworts, or *Pinguiculas*. *Pinguicula vulgaris* grows on wet limestone rocks in the extreme northern part of the United States and in Canada. It is a small plant with a rosette of sessile, entire, spatulate or somewhat elliptical leaves, and sends up in early summer a scape with one violet-colored flower. The leaves are soft-fleshy and rather greasy to the touch, which accounts for both its Latin and common names. On the upper surface of the leaf are scattered glandular hairs to which insects adhere as in the sundew. When an insect is caught the hairs do not move as in the sundew but the edge of the leaf curves inward in such a way as to bring several hairs in contact with the insect. Between the glandular hairs are some shorter papillate or disk-like hairs which probably have the function of absorbing the digested proteins.

39. **Venus's Flytrap and the Bladderworts.**—Venus's flytrap (*Dionaea muscipula*) is a rather rare little plant that grows on wet sand in several places in North and South Carolina (Fig. 23). It has a rosette of leaves each of which possesses at its terminal end two oval-shaped lobes which are hinged together at the mid-rib and have long stiff teeth around the outer edge. On the upper surface of each lobe are three bristle-like hairs which are very sensitive. When one of these hairs is touched the lobes close suddenly like a trap. If an

Fig. 23.—Venus's flytrap.   (Photograph by B. W. Wells.)

insect touches one of the hairs, therefore, it is almost invariably caught in the trap. The stiff teeth along the edges of the trap interlock like the teeth of a bear trap and the two lobes press together with such force that the outline of the insect can often be seen from the outside. The insect is digested by protein-digesting enzymes, secreted by glands on the surfaces of the leaves, and the digested portions are absorbed by the leaf. The trap then slowly opens again. The whole process from the capture of the insect to the opening of the trap may take several days but there are sometimes victims in several traps of one plant at the same time.

The bladderworts (*Utricularia*) belong to the same family as the butterworts but they are quite different appearing plants. There are a considerable number of species, most of which grow in the water of ponds, swamps or bogs. Most of them are free-floating but a few are rooted in the mud along the edges of ponds. The floating forms are often entirely without roots but have very much dissected submersed leaves which serve as absorbing organs. On these submersed leaves are found numerous small bladders each with an opening at one end which is furnished with a valve-like lid and usually a few stiff bristles pointing inward, much like the entrance to an eel trap. Entrance to the bladders is easy and small water animals often swim into them. Once in, however, they cannot get out. The evidence that these animals are digested and absorbed by the plant is not yet conclusive, though it is highly probable. If future investigations should prove that they are not digested by the plant then this would be social rather than nutritive symbiosis, but if, as is likely, the animals are used as food by the bladderwort then this is an example of antagonistic nutritive disjunctive symbiosis.

40. **Pitcher Plants** (Fig. 24).—There are several genera of plants that have pitcher-like leaves. *Sarracenia purpurea*, which occurs in peat bogs, is our commonest native pitcher plant. It produces a cluster of radical, pitcher-shaped leaves, with a wing along one side and a rounded arching hood at the upper end. The leaves are usually attractively colored, yellowish-green and purple, and 10 to 20 cm. long. In June it sends up a flowering stem, 15 to 30 cm. high, bearing a single, large, deep purple flower. The leaves of *Sarracenia* are practically always partly filled with water, probably caught by them during rains. Entrance to the pitchers is easy and insects often go in, perhaps merely by chance or perhaps attracted by the bright colors. Once in, however,

it is almost impossible for an insect to crawl out because of the numerous hairs near the entrance which point downward. The insects, therefore, sooner or later, get into the water and drown.   No protein-digesting enzymes have yet been found in the pitchers of *Sarracenia* but it is believed that the plant absorbs the products of decay of the insects and that the symbiosis is thus of the same type as that of other insectivorous plants.

FIG. 24.—*Sarracenia minor.* A pitcher plant. (Photograph by B. W. Wells.)

It has been shown that at least four kinds of insects and several protozoa live normally in the water in the pitchers of *Sarracenia purpurea.* In some species of *Sarracenia* frogs are often found resting in the pitchers and catching such insects as enter. Also, spiders sometimes spin webs across the mouths of pitchers for the purpose of catching insects. These relationships are comparable to a squirrel inhabiting a hole in a tree and would be classed as social disjunctive symbiosis.

Nepenthes is a genus of climbing or epiphytic plants of tropical Asia. The pitchers at the ends of the leaves of these plants have nectar glands just within the rim which serve to attract insects. The inner surface is extremely smooth and the insects in getting at the nectar usually slip and fall into the liquid below. The liquid in these pitchers has been shown to contain protein-digesting enzymes.

Dischidia, an epiphytic pitcher plant of the Malayan region, has two pitchers, one within the other. Soil and water collect in the outer pitcher and it thus serves as a sort of living flower-pot into which adventitious roots from other parts of the plant grow. The symbiotic relations of *Dischidia* have not been very thoroughly studied but they probably are similar to those of other pitcher plants.

REFERENCES.

Bailey, I. W.: Some Relations Between Ants and Fungi, Ecology, 1920, **1**, 174–189, 3 Pl.

Bequaert, J.: Ants in Their Diverse Relations to the Plant World, Bull. Am. Mus. Nat. Hist., 1922, **45**, 333–583.

Bose, S. R.: The Fungi Cultivated by Termites of Burkunda, Chilka Lake, India, Rec. Indian Mus., 1923, **25**, 253–258.

Buller, A. H. R.: The Red Squirrel of North America as a Mycophagist, Trans. British Mycol. Soc., 1920, **5**, 355–362.

Buller, A. H. R.: Slugs as Mycophagists, Trans. British Mycol. Soc., 1922, **7**, 270–293.

Darwin, Charles: Insectivorous Plants. D. Appleton & Co., New York, 1895.

Hegner, R. W.: The Interrelations of Protozoa and the Utricles of Utricularia, Biol. Bull. Marine Biol. Lab., 1926, **50**, 239–270.

Howard, A.: The Effect of Grass on Trees, Proc. Roy. Soc. London, 1925, B**97**, 284–321.

McDougall, W. B.: The Classification of Symbiotic Phenomena, Plant World, 1918, **21**, 250–256.

McDougall, W. B.: Symbiosis in a Deciduous Forest, Bot. Gaz., 1922, **73**, 200–212; 1925, **79**, 95–102.

CHAPTER VI.

POLLINATION.

POLLINATION is the transfer of pollen grains to the stigma, or, in the case of gymnosperms, to the ovule. In the very great majority of cases it is brought about by some external agency. The principal agents of pollination are animals, wind and water. The cases in which pollination is brought about through the agency of animals represent our commonest examples of reciprocal nutritive disjunctive symbiosis and these will be discussed in Chapter VII. The present chapter treats of pollination through non-living agencies and, therefore, does not deal with symbiosis. It is interpolated here between two chapters on symbiosis for the sake of convenience in discussing all types of pollination in sequence.

41. **Cross and Close Pollination.**—When a flower is pollinated with pollen derived from a flower of a separate plant the phenomenon is called cross pollination or xenogamy, while, if the flower is pollinated with its own pollen, it is called close pollination or autogamy. A condition that is intermediate between autogamy and xenogamy is that in which the pollen is derived from another flower on the same plant. This is called geitonogamy.

In some plants autogamy is the only kind of pollination that is possible. This is obviously true of flowers that never open, such as the cleistogamous flowers produced by several species of violets and by a number of other plants. In other plants, and probably a much greater number, only xenogamy is possible. In the great majority of plants, however, it is probable that both autogamy, or geitonogamy, and xenogamy are possible. Xenogamy is never possible except through the

(82)

aid of some external agent and with relatively few exceptions this is true also of geitonogamy. Even in autogamy gravity, wind, water, or animals often bring about pollination and in many cases one of these agencies is absolutely essential. In some cases of autogamy, however, pollination is brought about by actual contact between the stamens and stigmas. Strictly speaking these are the only cases of self-pollination. In practice, however, all cases of autogamy and geitonogamy are ordinarily called self-pollination as opposed to cross pollination which includes all cases of xenogamy, that is, all cases in which the pollen is derived from a separate plant.

42. **Wind Pollination.**—Flowers that are pollinated by the wind are ordinarily called anemophilous (wind-loving) flowers. Wind pollination is in certain respects the simplest form of pollination, although the flowers are often as perfectly adapted for it, structurally, as are the flowers that depend upon animals for pollination. The staminate flowers are often in catkins which hang downward and yield pollen, when it is ready, to the slightest breeze. Staminate catkins are especially characteristic of many trees and shrubs where they are well exposed to the wind. In most of the woody plants that are wind pollinated the flowers are produced early in the spring before the leaves expand so that there is very little in the way of the wind. In some wind-pollinated plants the pistillate flowers are also in catkins but in many they are not and probably there is no advantage in having the pistillate flowers in this type of inflorescence.

In many wind-pollinated flowers that are not arranged in catkins the stamens have such long and slender filaments that the anthers hang entirely outside of the flowers and so are freely exposed to the wind. Also, in the majority of wind-pollinated flowers, if we except the grass and sedge families, the pollen is produced in great abundance. It is important that this should be so because the wind is a very wasteful agent. It scatters the pollen indiscriminately, far and wide, and only a very small percentage of the pollen grains land by chance upon the stigmas of flowers belonging to the same species from which the pollen came. The pollen of anemophilous flowers is in most cases light, smooth, and dry, and thus is easily blown about by the wind. As a rule, too, they are not easily wetted; a fact of importance in rainy weather since wet pollen could not be blown about readily. The stigmas are usually large and well exposed and so are suitably fitted for catching wind-blown pollen.

As a rule anemophilous flowers are without odor and nectar, contrasting with insect-pollinated flowers in these respects, and also, in the majority of cases, in a lack of showiness. The perianth is usually inconspicuous, either because of its greenish or brownish color or because of its small size, and in many cases it is absent entirely. When a perianth is present it usually consists of a calyx only, the presence of a corolla in wind-pollinated flowers being relatively rare.

43. **Cross Pollination in Anemophilous Flowers.**—Although wind-pollinated flowers are as a rule more simple structurally than are those pollinated by animals yet they are in many cases as well fitted for cross pollination as are the more complex insect-pollinated flowers.

Plants that have their stamens and pistils in the same flowers (perfect flowers) are said to be monoclinous, while those that have these essential organs in separate flowers (imperfect flowers) are diclinous. Diclinous plants are further subdivided into monœcious, those which have the stamens and pistils in separate flowers on the same plant, and diœcious, those that have their stamens and pistils on separate plants.

Very many, probably a majority, of wind-pollinated plants are diclinous and many of these are diœcious. In the diœcious forms, of course, nothing but xenogamy is possible. In monœcious forms either xenogamy or geitonogamy is possible but in many cases the pistillate flowers are placed higher on the plant than the staminate and this makes geitonogamy very unlikely. The likelihood of geitonogamy is still further minimized in most cases by the fact that the pistillate flowers on any individual plant bloom earlier, sometimes several days earlier, than the staminate flowers of the same individual.

When the stamens and pistils of a monoclinous flower mature at different times the phenomenon is known as dichogamy. Dichogamy is subdivided into protogyny, the maturing of the stigmas before the anthers, and protandry, the maturing of the anthers before the stigmas. Both protandry and protogyny are found among monoclinous wind-pollinated plants and make cross pollination rather certain among those plants that exhibit it.

Still another, and even more specialized, means of insuring cross pollination is found in a few anemophilous plants as, for example, in rye. In this plant the pollen is impotent, that is it will not germinate, on the stigma of the same flower in which it was produced but will germinate readily on the stigma of any other plant of the species.

44. **Some Wind-pollinated Flowers.**—Many of our common trees and shrubs which produce their flowers, at least the staminate ones, in catkins, and which bloom early in spring, often before the leaves have developed, are wind-pollinated. Among these are the poplars, birches, oaks, hickories, walnuts, hazels and alders. The poplars are diœcious and it is necessary, therefore, that pollen be blown from one tree to another. The stamens of these plants are elastic and when the weather is clear and dry the pollen is discharged forcibly into the air to a distance of several inches. This gives it a good start on its journey. The birches, on the other hand, are monœcious, with both kinds of flowers in catkins (Fig. 25). The oaks, hickories, walnuts and hazels are also monœcious but have only their staminate flowers in catkins. The pistillate flowers are either solitary or only a few in a cluster.

Among other trees that are wind-pollinated are the beeches, elms and ashes. In the beech the pistillate flowers are in pairs while the staminate flowers are clustered in globose heads, 2 or 3 cm. in diameter, which hang downward at the ends of long slender peduncles. The flowers of the elm are borne in small loose clusters. They are mostly perfect and

Fig. 25.—Yellow birch (*Betula lutea*). Wind pollinated. Staminate catkins above, pistillate below. (Photograph by John H. Lovell.)

close pollination is largely prevented by protogyny. Some species of ash are diœcious while others are monoclinous and still others are both, but in any case the flowers are all clustered on the branches.

All of the conifers are wind pollinated (Figs. 26 and 27). They are all diclinous and most of them are monœcious though a few are diœcious. Pollen is produced by coniferous

Fig. 26.—Red pine (*Pinus resinosa*). Staminate cones. (From The Flower and the Bee, by John H. Lovell; copyright, 1918, by Charles Scribner's Sons. By permission of author and publisher.)

trees extremely abundantly. Great clouds of pollen sometimes arise from pine forests in such a way as to appear like smoke columns. Such immense numbers of pollen grains settle down on foliage, branches, grass and soil that the whole

landscape is given a yellowish color.   Such a phenomenon is
often spoken of as a "sulphur shower."   The pollen grains
of pine are so well adapted to dissemination by the wind that

Fig. 27.—Red pine (*Pinus resinosa*). Ovulate cones. Wind pollinated.
(From The Flower and the Bee, by John H. Lovell; copyright, 1918, by
Charles Scribner's Sons. By permission of author and publisher.)

some have been known to be carried more than 100 miles.
Since everything in the neighborhood of the forest is covered
with pollen some of the grains inevitably come in contact
with the ovules in the pistillate cones and this constitutes
pollination.

Two other important groups of plants that are anemophilous are the grasses and sedges. The majority of the grasses are monoclinous and self-pollination is often, though not always, prevented by dichogamy. Some, however, such as Indian corn, are diclinous and monœcious or, in a few cases, diœcious. Some of the sedges are monoclinous also, but probably a greater number are diclinous. Most of the diclinous species are monœcious but a few are diœcious. Many of the grasses bloom early in the morning, at sunrise or a little later, and it is an interesting phenomenon to watch. The bracts spread apart, the stamens elongate until the anthers hang outside of the flower, and then the pollen is shed, the whole process often taking no more than fifteen or twenty minutes. As a rule each flower remains open but a short time but different flowers on the same plant may open progressively for several days. Sometimes unfavorable weather greatly retards or prevents the opening of the flowers and in that case self-pollination is likely to occur.

45. **Water Pollination.**—The majority of seed plants that grow in the water produce their flowers above the surface of the water and are pollinated by the wind or by insects. There are some interesting cases, however, in which water is the agent of pollination. In some of the pondweeds (*Potamogeton*), for example, the pollen grains are filamentous and without thick walls. They are just heavy enough to float below the surface of the water and may come in contact with the long exserted stigmas by chance.

In the tape grass (*Vallisneria spiralis*) the solitary pistillate flowers are borne on peduncles which elongate just enough to bring the flowers to the surface of the water. Sometimes these peduncles become as much as a meter in length, the growth continuing in any particular case until it is checked, probably, by increased transpiration at the surface of the water. The staminate flowers are produced in clusters of several hundred. Each one is about 1 mm. in diameter and consists of two stamens enclosed in a three-parted perianth.

These staminate flowers become detached under water and rise slowly to the surface where they open and the segments of the perianth curve back in such a way as to support the flower on a little tripod. A pistillate flower resting on the surface of the water causes a slight depression of the surface film and when staminate flowers approach this depression by chance they shoot down into it and the stamens are very likely to come into contact with the stigmas. After pollination has taken place the peduncle coils up and draws the pistillate flower below the surface again, where the fruit matures.

Another interesting case of pollination in water plants is that found in some of the duckweeds. The duckweeds are among the smallest and simplest of flowering plants. One of these, *Lemna minor*, consists of a little green thallus from 2 to 5 mm. in diameter which floats on the surface of the water. Projecting into the water from the under side of the thallus is a single little rootlet, so reduced that it contains no vascular tissue. This simple little plant produces a cluster of 3 flowers, 2 staminate and 1 pistillate, in a notch in one side of the thallus. Each staminate flower consists of a single stamen and nothing else while the pistillate flower consists of a single pistil and the three are enclosed in a spathe in such a way as to appear like a single flower with two stamens and one pistil. The pistillate flower matures first and is ready to receive pollen several days before either of the staminate flowers is ready to expose its pollen. One of the stamens then elongates and the anther opens, the pollen remaining heaped in the open pollen sacs. Several days later the second stamen matures and exposes its pollen. Usually there are hundreds of individuals of these plants crowded together and they are constantly being jostled against one another by movements of the water due to wind or other causes. The open anthers are thus almost certain to be brought into contact with receptive stigmas. The dichogamy exhibited by this plant makes cross pollination almost certain but the stigma is still receptive when the first stamen matures so that if it has not already been pollinated self-pollination may take place at that time.

REFERENCES.

Coulter, J. M., Barnes, C. E. and Cowles, H. C.: A Text-book of Botany. Vol. II. Ecology. Chapter V. Reproduction and Dispersal, American Book Company, 1911.

Rodrigo, P. A.: Pollination and the Flowers of Rice, Philippine Agric., 1925, **14**, 155–171.

Skene, Macgregor: The Biology of Flowering Plants. Chapter V. Reproduction and Dispersal, The Macmillan Company, 1924.

Wylie, R. B.: The Pollination of Vallisneria Spiralis, Bot. Gaz., 1917, **63**, 135–145.

CHAPTER VII.

RECIPROCAL NUTRITIVE DISJUNCTIVE SYMBIOSIS.

In reciprocal nutritive disjunctive symbiosis one or more, but not necessarily all, of the organisms concerned obtain food from one or more of the others, but those that lose food and get none in return are nevertheless benefited by the relationship in some other way so that the symbiosis is reciprocal so far as actual benefit derived from it is concerned. The outstanding examples are those concerned with pollination by means of animals, especially insects, and with dissemination through the aid of animals, especially birds and ants. The subject of dissemination, like that of pollination, falls under the general term symbiosis only in part. Furthermore it is closely related to the development of plant communities; a subject to be dealt with at length in later chapters. For these reasons it will be more convenient and also conducive to clearness to postpone all discussion of dissemination until we are ready to discuss vegetational development. The present chapter, therefore, will deal entirely with pollination by animals.

46. **Insect Pollination.**—Insects visit flowers, ordinarily, for the purpose of obtaining food, either nectar or pollen, and while accomplishing this purpose they incidentally affect pollination. These simple symbiotic relations between insects and the flowers they visit involve some of the most remarkable phenomena in the whole realm of Nature. No evolutionary facts are more astounding or more nearly inexplicable than that the flowers of many species of plants remain unpollinated unless they are visited by insects; in some cases by a particular kind of insect.

(92)

The great majority of insect-pollinated, or entomophilous, flowers are monoclinous. This is probably a distinct advantage since it makes possible twice as many acts of pollination for a given number of insect visits than if the flowers were diclinous. That is, in the case of diclinous flowers it is necessary for the insect to visit two flowers, a staminate and a pistillate, in order to accomplish one act of pollination, while in monoclinous flowers it is possible in each visit after the first one to deposit pollen on the stigma and at the same time collect more pollen from the stamens. Furthermore insects which were bent only on gathering pollen would, of course, not visit flowers that were only pistillate at all.

In many respects insect-pollinated flowers contrast sharply with those that are wind-pollinated (Fig. 28). The flowers as a rule are not in catkins but rather in inflorescences that are relatively inflexible in the wind. The stamens have relatively short filaments and are usually not prominently exserted. The pollen, instead of being dry and smooth, as in anemophilous flowers, is often rough with spines or other protuberances, or viscid, or both. This causes the grains to stick together in masses, renders them less easily blown about by the wind, and adapts them admirably to sticking to the legs and bodies of insects as well as to stigmatic surfaces.

Flowers that are wide open and have their parts freely exposed can usually be pollinated by most any kind of visiting insect. They often have numerous stamens and produce pollen as abundantly as many wind-pollinated species. Those that have the pollen partly or wholly concealed in tubular or otherwise partly closed corollas, however, usually have few stamens and do not produce pollen abundantly. The stigmas of insect-pollinated flowers as compared to those of wind-pollinated flowers are small and inconspicuous.

Insect-pollinated flowers are further characterized by showiness. This may be due either to color, size, form or arrangement, or to two or more of these features combined.

In many cases, also, they are characterized by fragrance or by the production of nectar, or both.

47. Cross Pollination in Entomophilous Flowers.—The majority of insect-pollinated flowers exhibit dichogamy to a greater

FIG. 28.—*Frasera speciosa*, with insect-pollinated flowers.

or less degree. In some cases the dichogamy is complete, that is, the stigmas are not receptive at any time when the stamens of the same flower are discharging pollen (Fig. 29). More often, however, there is some overlapping so that, if cross pollination has failed to occur, close or self-pollination

LEGEND FOR FIG. 29, PAGE 95.

FIG. 29.—Fire weed (*Epilobium augustifolium*). Life history of flowers showing protandry. (After Clements and Long.)

only by bees and such plants are limited in their distribution to those regions that are inhabited by bees.

Ants are of no importance as pollinating agents and wasps, as compared with bees, are of minor importance, although there are some flowers, notably those of the figs, that are pollinated only by wasps.

Next to the Hymenoptera, in importance as pollinating agents, are the Lepidoptera, or butterflies and moths. These are nectar feeders only and their mouth parts are very greatly specialized and elongated to enable them to obtain nectar from long corolla tubes. The butterflies which fly during the day and visit mostly showy and fragrant flowers are rather haphazard in their movements. They are apt to visit several different species of flowers within a few minutes and for that reason are not very efficient pollinators. Some of the moths, on the other hand, especially the hawk moths, are as precise in their movements as bees. The moths are night-flying insects and visit mostly night-blooming flowers. The hawk moths have very long mouth parts, sometimes as much as 7 or 8 cm. in length, which are coiled up when not in use. They visit mostly fragrant, white flowers with long corolla tubes.

The majority of the flies are of no importance as pollinating agents. The syrphid flies, however, which look a great deal like bees, feed largely upon nectar and pollen and so are of considerable importance. The carrion flies are also of some importance especially in connection with the pollination of ill-smelling flowers. They seem to be attracted particularly by odors that are offensive to human beings. A few kinds of beetles sometimes affect pollination but as a rule the floral visits of beetles result in more harm than good.

49. Color, Odor and Memory in Insect Pollination.—A great deal of work has been done during the past one hundred and fifty years in efforts to determine the relative importance of color, form, odor and memory in attracting or directing insects, especially bees, to flowers, and a great deal has been

written on the subject.   Much more needs to be done before
we can speak with certainty on all phases of the question but
certain facts are now fairly well established.

Many experiments have been performed for the purpose
of determining whether bees can recognize colors, such, for
instance, as removing the corollas of flowers, using artificial
flowers, painting flowers unusual colors, or enclosing flowers
in glass, and then observing the activities of the bees.   While
there has been some disagreement among different workers,
the most reliable results show that bees do readily distinguish
colors.   Honey-bees show a decided preference for blue, but,
when working on any particular species, they show a preference for the color of that species whatever it may be.   It has
also been shown, however, that they discriminate between
colors only when it is of advantage to do so.   In the case of
a species with variable colors they soon learn that color
discrimination is unnecessary and so they depend entirely
upon form and odor.   Charles Darwin once remarked that
bees are very good botanists since they know that different
varieties of the same species may differ widely in color.   On
the other hand, bees do distinguish species partly on the
basis of color and they also depend on color to a certain
extent to distinguish between fresh flowers and old withered
ones or partly opened buds.   When part of the flowers of a
species are painted unusual colors the bees show a decided
preference for the natural color until experience teaches them
that such discrimination is unnecessary.   It is pretty generally agreed also that the power of vision of bees is sufficiently
developed to enable them to readily recognize differences in
form and patterns of flowers.   In fact they seem to be able to
distinguish differences in surface and texture that are so
small as to be unnoticed by man.

The sense of odor of insects has often been over-emphasized,
although it differs greatly in different groups.   Honey-bees
do not have a sense of smell that is especially highly developed and when they are in the immediate vicinity of flowers

color and form are much more important than odor in guiding them. It is true also, of course, that bees cannot see for great distances. It seems to be true, therefore, that for distances greater than 20 meters odor is more important than color and form, while, for intermediate distances, color in mass is most used, and for distances of 1 meter or less the color and form of individual flowers are the guiding factors. For distances that are measured in miles, however, bees have simply to go hunting for flowers just as men do. But it is true also that memory and habit play important roles and when bees have once found a field of clover or a basswood tree they make subsequent trips to the same place with apparently no more trouble than a man would have.

50. **Bee Flowers.**—Flowers which are wide open and have their pollen and often their nectaries freely accessible are visited by a variety of insect species any of which may affect pollination. There are many flowers, however, that are partly closed, that are very irregular in shape, or that have their nectar concealed, which can be pollinated by only one or a few species of insects.

Some of the violets are bee flowers, that is, they are pollinated almost entirely by bees. This is true especially of some of the yellow violets and of the cultivated pansies (*Viola tricolor*). Most of the blue violets, on the other hand, are not much visited by insects and are often infertile. These species, in addition to the blue flowers, produce, usually later in the season, small green flowers (called cleistogamous flowers) which never open, are self-pollinated and produce seed abundantly.

The legume family contains a very large number of bee flowers, several of which never produce seeds unless visited by bees. Many members of this family have 9 of the 10 stamens united into a tube and the nectar, if any is present, is at the bottom of the tube. Four of the petals, the 2 forming the keel and the 2 wing petals, are interlocked, around the stamen tube, while the fifth, called the standard is broad and more or less erect. When a bee visits the flower for nectar it rests on the wing petals, which act as levers, and, bracing its head against the standard, depresses the keel enough so it can reach the nectar with its mouth parts. While it is doing this pollen is applied to the under side of its body. If the bee is not strong enough to depress the keel it, of course, does not get the nectar. Very few bees are strong enough to depress the keel of a sweet-pea flower and for that reason sweet-pea flowers are not much visited by bees and are usually self-pollinated.

The flower of alfalfa has the anthers and stigma held in the keel under tension and when a bee presses the keel down the anthers and stigma fly forcibly upward against the body of the insect. It is a curious fact that east of the Mississippi River alfalfa does not produce much nectar while in the western part of the United States it is one of the most prolific of honey plants. The honey-bees that visit alfalfa flowers, however, usually do not affect pollination since they steal the nectar through a hole in the side of the corolla. In such a case the symbiosis is antagonistic and not reciprocal.

Red clover (*Trifolium pratense*) is pollinated almost entirely by bumble-bees and does not produce seed in the absence of bumble-bees, except in occasional years when *Tetralonia*, one of the solitary bees, is abundant. Honey-bees, as a rule, are unable to get nectar from red clover because their mouth parts are not long enough to reach it. Occasionally, in very dry years, the floral tubes of red clover are short enough so that honey-bees can reach the nectar and red clover fields yield an abundance of honey, but ordinarily this plant is not a good honey plant. White clover (*Trifolium repens*), on the other hand, is one of the best of honey plants wherever it grows (Figs. 30 and 31). Other common bumble-bee flowers are the larkspurs (*Delphinium*), the columbines (*Aquilegia*), the jewelweeds (*Impatiens*), and the snapdragons (*Antirrhinum*) (Fig. 32). The mint family and the figwort family also contain many bee flowers.   In these families the pollen is deposited on the backs of the insects instead of on the underside of the body as in the legume family.

Fig. 30.—White clover (*Trifolium repens*), a bee flower.   After pollination the flowers all bend downward and turn reddish, then brown.   See Fig. 31.   (From The Flower and the Bee, by John H. Lovell; copyright, 1918, by Charles Scribner's Sons.   By permission of author and publisher.)

51. Butterfly and Moth Flowers.—While blue seems to be the favorite color with bees there are a very large number of flowers pollinated largely by butterflies that are some shade of red.   The pink family (*Caryophyllaceæ*) contains a considerable number of butterfly flowers, some of which are almost entirely dependent upon butterflies for pollination since their nectar is hidden so deeply that it cannot be reached by other insects. The wild orange-red lily (*Lilium philadelphicum*) is another butterfly flower. It grows on dry uplands and produces flowers that are upright and well

Fig. 31.—White clover (*Trifolium repens*). Final stage, flowers all reflexed and brown colored. (Photograph by John H. Lovell.)

adapted to pollination by butterflies. Its relative (*Lilium canadense*) which grows in low places along streams has yellow flowers which are inverted. Because of their inverted position they are not easily visited by butterflies and are pollinated by bees almost entirely. Other butterfly flowers include several species of *Phlox* (Fig. 33) and numerous orchids. Many composites are pollinated by butterflies but they are not strictly butterfly flowers since they may be pollinated by various kinds of insects.

FIG. 32.—Fringed gentian (*Gentiana crinita*). A bumble-bee flower. (From The Flower and the Bee, by John H. Lovell; copyright, 1918, by Charles Scribner's Sons. By permission of author and publisher.)

The hawk moths, being night-flying insects, visit mostly white, fragrant, night-blooming flowers. The Jimson weed (*Datura tatula*) and the night-blooming tobacco (*Nicotiana noctiflora*) are good examples of hawk-moth flowers. Not all hawk-moth flowers are white, however. The evening primrose (*Œnothera biennis*), for example, which is yellow, is pollinated largely by these insects.

Perhaps the most interesting of all cases of pollination by moths is that of the yuccas which are pollinated by small

FIG. 33.—Red phlox (*Phlox paniculata*). A butterfly flower. (From The Flower and the Bee, by John H. Lovell; copyright, 1918, by Charles Scribner's Sons. By permission of author and publisher.)

moths belonging to the genus *Pronuba*. The flowers of the yuccas are pendulous and the style hangs down farther than the stamens but it is impossible for the pollen to fall from the anthers to the stigma because the stigma is cup-shaped

and the stigmatic portion is on the inner surface only. The
female moths begin work soon after sundown. Each one
collects some pollen from the anthers and holds it in her
specially constructed mouth parts. She then usually flies
to another flower, pierces the ovary with her ovipositor, and,
after laying one or more eggs, creeps down the style and

Fig. 34.—Dutchman's pipe (*Aristolochia macrophylla*). A fly flower.
(From The Flower and the Bee, by John H. Lovell; copyright, 1918, by
Charles Scribner's Sons. By permission of author and publisher.)

stuffs a ball of pollen into the stigma. It is difficult to
imagine what would cause a moth to stuff pollen into a
stigma for one hesitates to believe that she knows what the
result will be. Yet this symbiotic relation is obligate for
both the yucca and the moth, since in the absence of the
moth the yucca produces no seed while without the yucca

the moth cannot complete its life cycle, and if the moths should fail to pollinate the yuccas the result would ultimately be the extinction of both plant and insect. The yucca produces a very large number of ovules. Part of these are eaten by the moth larvæ and the remainder mature into seeds

52. Fly Flowers.—Syrphid flies, and some other nectar-feeding flies, visit many of the same flowers that are frequented by bees and such flowers cannot, of course, be

Fig. 35.—Skunk cabbage (*Symplocarpus fœtidus*). A fly flower.

designated strictly as fly flowers. Syrphid flies are especially important as pollinators of some fruit trees, though these trees may also be pollinated by bees. There are some flowers, however, that are pollinated almost exclusively by flies (Fig. 34). Many of these are ill-smelling and attract mainly carrion flies. Familiar examples are the carrion flower (*Smilax herbacea*), the purple trillium (*Trillium erectum*), the skunk cabbage (*Symplocarpus fœtidus*) (Fig. 35) and the water arum (*Calla palustris*).

There are some fly flowers that are sometimes spoken of as

prison, or pitfall, flowers. The spotted arum (*Arum macula-tum*), a native of Europe, is one of these. This plant has its flowers on a spadix in a spathe, in a manner comparable to our Jack-in-the-pulpit. The pistillate flowers are near the base of the spadix. A little higher up are the staminate flowers and a short distance above the staminate flowers the spathe is constricted. There is a cluster of hairs on the spadix at the point where the spathe is constricted. These point downward and practically fill the spathe at that point. There is also a similar cluster of hairs between the group of staminate flowers and the pistillate flowers.

The small flies which bring about pollination in this plant easily enter the spathe and pass down to the pistillate flowers where they feed upon the nectar. Their exit, however, is prevented by the stiff hairs. The pistillate flowers mature first and the lowest cluster of hairs then withers. This permits the flies to come up to the staminate flowers where they become dusted with pollen. Later the upper ring of hairs withers and the insects are liberated and are free to fly to another flower.

The Jack-in-the-pulpit (*Arisæma triphyllum*), which belongs to the same family as the *Arum*, is also somewhat of a prison flower. This species is diœcious and the staminate plants mature a little in advance of the pistillate. The spathes are extremely smooth and slippery on the inner side. The flies are very likely to visit a staminate inflorescence first and once inside the spathe they are unable to climb up the smooth walls or the equally smooth spadix. As soon as the spathe begins to wither, however, it becomes less smooth and the flies escape and may chance then to visit a pistillate plant and so affect pollination. In the pistillate inflorescence they are again imprisoned until the spathe begins to wither. This does not take place so promptly as in the case of the staminate plant and often the insects perish before they are liberated.

53. **Pollination of the Fig.**—One of the strangest of the known cases of symbiosis between flowers and insects is that

of the commercial fig and the wasps of the genus *Blastophaga* which pollinate it. The flowers of the fig are produced in composite inflorescences called syconia. A syconium consists of a fleshy receptacle which has developed into a hollow structure with a very small orifice at the upper end. The numerous flowers are arranged on the inner side, which is the morphological upper side, of the receptacle. The flowers are diclinous and the plants are essentially diœcious. The pistillate syconia, which are called figs, contain only normal pistillate flowers with rather long styles, while the staminate syconia, called caprifigs, contain both staminate flowers and small, short-styled, pistillate flowers, which are known as gall flowers. Pollination of the fig is accomplished by the female wasps. The orifices of the syconia are so nearly closed by over-lapping scales that the wasps have great difficulty in getting in and often tear off their wings in the process. After a wasp has entered a pistillate syconium she creeps over the flowers searching for a suitable place to lay eggs and while doing this the pollen on her body is rubbed onto the stigmas. The styles of the flowers are so long, however, that the wasp is unable to reach the ovaries with her ovipositor and so is unable to lay any eggs. She cannot get out of the syconium, however, and soon perishes, but the flowers, having been pollinated, continue their normal development and the syconium matures into a fig.

If, on the other hand, the wasp chances to enter a caprifig she readily reaches the ovaries of the short-styled gall flowers and lays her eggs there. She then perishes in the caprifig. When the eggs hatch the young wasps feed upon the tissues of the gall flowers and, when mature, the males eat their way out of the ovaries in which they hatched and into those occupied by the females. After mating with the females the males soon die without leaving the caprifigs. The females now become dusted with pollen, make their way to the exterior, and fly to another syconium. Those that by chance enter figs will affect pollination but will not leave any offspring, while those that enter caprifigs will leave offspring but will not affect pollination. This symbiosis is obligate for both the plant and the insect yet the course of the evolution that has brought about so strange a relationship can scarcely even be imagined.

54. **Pollination by Birds and Other Animals.**—Next to insects, birds are the most important pollinating animals. Bird pollination seems to be more important in the southern hemisphere than in the northern. In South America the numerous humming birds are important pollinators while in Africa the sun birds are more important. The characteristics of bird flowers are in general similar to those that we are familiar with in bee flowers.

A few cases of pollination by bats have been reported but neither these nor any other animals are important as compared with birds, and more especially with insects, as pollinating agents.

REFERENCES.

Bouquet, A. G. B.: Pollination of Tomatoes, Oregon Agric. Exp. Sta. Bull., 1919, **157**, 1–29.

Burkill, I. H.: Insect Vision in Connection with Flower Fertilization, Singapore Nat., 1925, **5**, 23–46.

Clements, Frederic E., and Long, Frances L.: Experimental Pollination: an Outline of the Ecology of Flowers and Insects, Carnegie Inst. Washington Publ., 1923, **336**, 274 p. 37 pl.

Hazen, T. E.: The Trimorphism and Insect Visitors of *Pontederia*, Mem. Torrey Bot. Club, 1917, **17**, 459–484.

Hendrickson, A. H.: The Common Honey Bee as an Agent in Prune Pollination, California Agric. Exp. Sta. Bull., 1918, **291**, 215–236, 13 fig.

Lovell, John H.: The Flower and the Bee, Charles Scribner's Sons, New York, 1918, 286 p. 119 fig.

Lutz, Frank E.: The Color of Flowers and the Vision of Insects, with Special Reference to Ultra-violet, Ann. New York Acad. Sci., 1914, **29**, 233–283, pl. 3–9, fig. 24–48.

Marsden-Jones, E. N.: On the Pollination of *Primula vulgaris*, Huds. Jour. Linn. Soc. London. Bot., 1926, **47**, 367–381.

Newcombe, F. C.: Significance of the Behavior of Sensitive Stigmas, Am. Jour. Bot., 1922, **9**, 99–120.

Pellett, Frank C.: American Honey Plants, American Bee Journal, Hamilton, Illinois, 1923, 392 p. 194 fig.

Rock, J. F.: Nectar-feeding Birds of Hawaii, Jour. Heredity, 1921, **12**, 281–284, 2 fig.

Schuster, C. E.: Pollination and the Growing of the Cherry, Oregon Agric. Exp. Sta. Bull., 1925, **212**, 1–40.

Small, J.: The Origin and Development of the Compositæ II. The Pollen-presentation Mechanism, New Phytologist, 1917, **16**, 198–221.

CHAPTER VIII.

SOCIAL CONJUNCTIVE SYMBIOSIS.

CONJUNCTIVE symbiosis includes all cases of the living together of two or more unlike organisms in which the symbionts are in actual contact throughout the time during which they are said to be in a state of symbiosis. Any example of conjunctive symbiosis in which there is no direct food relation between any of the symbionts may be classed as social. The commonest examples of social conjunctive symbiosis are those of the various kinds of climbing plants and of plants that grow upon other plants for support but without deriving food from their hosts.

55. **Lianas.**—Lianas are plants that climb by one means or another (Fig. 36). They do not have a sufficient amount of mechanical tissue to maintain themselves in an upright position and so are forced to climb upon some support in order to display their foliage in an adequate way. If the support happens to be another plant, as it does in a great majority of cases, the phenomenon represents a symbiotic relation between the liana and its host.

The number of species of lianas in the north temperate zone is comparatively small but in tropical forests, where they reach their maximum development, the wealth of species is astonishingly great. Certain families, such as the legume, moonseed, soapberry, and Bignonia families are especially rich in climbing species, but a very large number of other families contain some lianas. In some tropical forests the lianas rank next to the trees themselves in conspicuousness. They vary greatly in size and in habit. They may be closely twisted around large or small stems or they may hang as streamers from the branches of trees. Some are stretched tightly from one tree to another while others loop downward to form great festoons from one branch to another. In many cases, too, they occur tangled together in masses on the ground.

The internal structure of the stems of lianas is characteristically different from that of upright stems. Especially is this true of twining plants the stems of which are neces-

FIG. 36.—Wild grape climbing on *Cratœgus*. Social conjunctive symbiosis.

sarily pliable. In such stems the wood is seldom continuous but is separated into distinct wedges which frequently become much lobed and cleft as secondary growth proceeds. Sometimes the wood is also separated radially, the cambium being periodically renewed outward in the cortex, with the result that concentric zones of wood separated by rings of fundamental tissue are produced. In many lianas the internal structure shows an eccentric or a flattened arrangement due to the constant lateral pressure against the host.

The internodes of lianas are usually long, and the longest and largest known tracheæ occur in certain climbing stems. Such vessels appear to be correlated with the necessity of transporting water to great heights through a stem that is relatively small.

56. **Twiners.**—Twining plants are perhaps the most specialized of lianas. In these the tip of the shoot executes a rotating movement known as circumnutation. This movement is induced and regulated by the response of the stem tip to the force of gravity and causes the stem to twine about any suitable support. The movement is due to a more rapid growth on one side of the stem. Since the twining of the stem necessarily results in a twisting on its axis the place of rapid growth is constantly changing and migrating around the stem. Each complete revolution of the tip is accompanied by a complete twist on the axis of the stem and the most rapid growth of any given area on the stem is induced when that area is lowermost.

The direction of twining is specific, that is, with a very few exceptions, all individuals of a given species twine in the same direction. In the majority of cases the direction is counter-clockwise while in a smaller number it is clockwise. Among plants that twine in a counter-clockwise direction are the bean (*Phaseolus*), the bittersweet (*Celastrus*), the moonseed (*Menispermum*), and the bittersweet nightshade (*Solanum dulcamara*). The hop (*Humulus*) and the black bindweed (*Polygonum scandens*) twine in a clockwise direction.

57. **Tendril Climbers.**—Scarcely second to the twiners in specialization are the tendril climbers in which one organ or another is modified into a tendril which grasps any support with which it comes in contact. Tendrils are ordinarily extremely sensitive to contact with solid bodies. In some cases merely stroking the tendril lightly with a match-stick once or twice will cause a bending of the tendril at the point of contact within a minute or two. Even contact with a

8

cotton thread, moved by light air currents, has been known to produce a reaction in a tendril.

The bending of the tendril is brought about through an increase in the rate of growth on the side opposite that stimulated, accompanied by a decrease in the rate on the side which receives the stimulus. As the tendril bends around the support new regions make contact with it and are stimulated. Thus the encircling continues until the entire tendril is coiled about the support. Often that part of the tendril between the climbing plant and its supporting host coils into the form of a coil spring. This actually serves as a spring, stretching out and closing again during wind storms in such a way as to greatly diminish the danger of being broken or torn away from the support.

Tendrils may be formed from very diverse morphological parts of plants but usually they are either leaves or parts of leaves, or branches. In the climbing *Tropæolum* the petioles serve as tendrils and are practically unmodified except in their sensitiveness to contact. A comparable condition is found in various species of *Clematis* where the stalks (*petiolules*) of the leaflets serve as tendrils. In the sweet pea and some other members of the legume family some of the terminal leaflets of the compound leaves are modified into tendrils. In *Smilax* the tendrils have the position of stipules. Since stipules are normally absent in monocotyledons, however, these tendrils are probably outgrowths from the leaf base. In the grape and other members of the Vitaceæ the tendrils are modified branches. In the squash and other members of the Cucurbitaceæ the origin of the tendrils is somewhat obscure, but it seems likely that, when they are simple, they are to be considered as modified leaves, and when they are branched, they represent shoots bearing leaves. Tendrils modified from roots are not common but are found in a few cases, as, for example, the orchid, *Vanilla*. In a few plants, especially some species of *Ampelopsis*, the tendrils do not twine about the support but form adhesive disks at their tips which cling to a solid surface with great tenacity.

58. Root Climbers and Leaners.—Climbing by means of roots is not very common among plants of the temperate zones but there are many tropical plants that climb by this

Fig. 37.—Poison ivy on hickory, climbing partly by twining and partly by adventitious roots. Since the ivy grows more rapidly than the hickory it is rapidly becoming too heavy for the host.

means. Familiar examples in the north temperate zone are the poison ivy (Fig. 37) and some varieties of the Virginia creeper (Fig. 38). These produce very large numbers of adventitious roots along their stems and these roots grow horizontally about the hosts as well as into the cracks and softer parts of the bark. Such success as these plants have in maintaining their positions is to be attributed to the large number of anchoring organs rather than to the efficiency of individual roots.

Fig. 38.—Trees covered with Virginia creeper (*Psedera quinquefolia*), a root climber.

Some plants, such as the bittersweet nightshade (*Solanum dulcamara*) do not have sufficient mechanical tissue to hold themselves erect and yet have no special means for climbing. Such plants often lean upon neighboring plants and may be spoken of as leaners. There are many plants which are prostrate when unsurrounded by other plants but which become leaners when growing in dense vegetation. Some leaners are kept from slipping from their supports by the presence of spines or prickles as in roses and blackberries. These are especially effective if they point downward as in the species of bedstraw (*Galium*).

59. **The Liana Habit.**—The chief advantage of the liana habit is that it enables a plant to get its leaves up into the light without constructing a large amount of mechanical tissue. The chief disadvantage is that it makes the climbing plant dependent. If the liana does not chance to find a suitable support to climb upon it cannot succeed in elevating its foliage much above the surface of the soil. Furthermore, if such a plant climbs upon a slow growing host it may in time become too heavy for its supporting plant and this in time may result in the downfall of both symbionts (Fig. 37). Sometimes the leaves of the liana overtop those of the host and cut off so much light that the host is gradually weakened and thus the downfall of both is hastened. (Fig. 36).

60. **Epiphytes.**—Epiphytes are plants that live upon other plants for support only. They are distinguished from parasites by the fact that they do not obtain food or food materials from the host plant. They manufacture their own food from carbon dioxide and water, and mineral salts that are derived mainly from wind blown and water-borne materials. They thus differ from ordinary land plants only in their symbiotic relation with a host and in their lack of any connection with the soil.

Epiphytes are especially characteristic of moist tropical regions. In some tropical forests tree-trunks and large branches of trees may be found that are as completely covered with vegetation as is the surface of the soil itself, and the mass of roots and soil on such a tree-trunk may be as much as a foot in thickness. While there are certain families of plants, such as the Orchidaceæ and Bromeliaceæ, which furnish unusually large numbers of epiphytes there are representatives among the epiphytes of many other seed-plant families as well as of ferns, mosses, liverworts, algæ, and lichens

(Fig. 39.) In regions with winters or long dry seasons epiphytes are relatively much less abundant and are limited almost entirely to the lower forms of life, epiphytic ferns and seed plants being absent from most regions outside of the moist tropics.

FIG. 39.—Spanish moss, an epiphytic seed plant on bald cypress in North Carolina.

Epiphytes very commonly possess certain structures that are characteristic of plants of dry climates, such as well-developed organs of absorption, structures for the storage of water, or modifications for preventing excessive transpiration. These characteristics are exhibited most markedly by epiphytes that occur near the tops of trees, where there is a high degree of exposure and progressively less by those lower down. In tropical forests where epiphytes are abundant there are certain species that occur only near the tops of the trees, others that occupy intermediate positions and still others that grow only lower down where the air is constantly humid.

In moist tropical forests certain kinds of epiphytes occur on leaves. These because of their position, are called epiphylls. Lichens, mosses, and even some vascular plants grow as epiphylls.

61. **Hemi-epiphytes and Pseudo-epiphytes.**—Hemi-epiphytes are plants that are epiphytic, and therefore symbiotic, during only a part of their lives. The strangling fig is a

Fig. 40.—Epiphytic fig on a *Palmetto* tree. (Photograph by William Trelease. Courtesy of Dr. George T. Moore and the Missouri Botanical Garden.)

notable example (Figs. 40 and 41). The seeds of the fig germinate on the bark of a host and the young fig plant starts its life as an epiphyte. Soon, however, some of its roots begin to grow downward and around the trunk of the host. These roots become thick and flattened and the host plant is often actually strangled by them (Fig. 42). Eventually they reach the soil and the fig then becomes an independent plant, no longer epiphytic (Figs. 43, 44 and 45).

Fig. 41.—*Palmetto* with two well-established figs, showing strangling roots that have reached the soil. (Photograph by William Trelease. Courtesy of Dr. George T. Moore and the Missouri Botanical Garden.)

Ordinary soil plants are often found growing in crotches or knotholes of trees where a little soil has collected. These are called pseudo-epiphytes. Their symbiotic relations to the host plant are comparable to those of true epiphytes.

62. The Epiphyte Habit.—Many epiphytes seem to be capable of growing on most any supporting host. Some can even grow upon non-living supports. Spanish moss (*Tillandsia*), for example, may grow hanging from telegraph wires if the air is sufficiently humid, and many mosses and

FIG. 42.—Strangling roots of an epiphytic fig. (Photograph by William Trelease. Courtesy of Dr. George T. Moore and the Missouri Botanical Garden.)

lichens grow equally well as epiphytes on living hosts or upon rocks. When growing upon rocks they are called lithophytes.

Some epiphytes, however, are more or less limited to certain kinds of hosts. The epiphytic fern, *Polypodium polypodioides* (Fig. 46), for example, is largely limited to trees having deeply-furrowed, soft bark which has a high water-absorbing capacity and loses water slowly. Such conditions are well provided by the American elm (*Ulmus Americana*) and the

Fig. 43.—Large fig tree with the *Palmetto* host still vigorous. (Photograph by William Trelease. Courtesy of Dr. George T. Moore and the Missouri Botanical Garden.)

post oak (*Quercus stellata*). In the case of epiphytic lichens it has long been known that the kinds that one may expect to find on a tree depends upon the character of the bark;

whether it is rough or smooth, hard or soft, resinous or non-resinous, etc.

It is doubtful whether any distinct advantage of the epiphytic habit can be noted. Often there is less competition for space than there is among land plants but it is open to

Fig. 44.—Large fig tree with *Palmetto* host almost killed. (Photograph by William Trelease. Courtesy of Dr. George T. Moore and the Missouri Botanical Garden.)

question whether this is a real advantage, and in many cases, especially in the tropics, there seems to be fully as much competition for space among epiphytes as among other plants. A very obvious disadvantage is the unfavorable position with respect to water supply.

Epiphytism frequently results in harm to the host plant.

Fig. 45.—Large fig tree with the *Palmetto* host completely gone. (Photograph by William Trelease. Courtesy of Dr. George T. Moore and the Missouri Botanical Garden.)

Fig. 46.—*Polypodium polypodioides*, an epiphytic fern growing on honey locust. (Photograph by L. J. Pessin.)

The strangling action of the hemi-epiphytic fig has already been mentioned. Other epiphytes frequently break down their hosts by their increasing weight or weaken them by cutting off a part of the light or by interfering with the free interchange of gases. Epiphylls are especially injurious in these latter ways.

REFERENCES.

Harris, J Authur: On the Osmotic Concentration of the Tissue Fluids of Phanerogamic Epiphytes, Am. Jour. Bot., 1918, **5**, 490–506.

Hendricks, H. V.: Torsion Studies in Twining Plants II, Bot. Gaz., 1923, **75**, 282–297, fig. 1–10.

Johnson, Duncan: Polypodium Vulgare as an Epiphyte, Bot. Gaz., 1921, **72**, 237–244, 3 fig.

Pessin, Louis J.: Epiphyllous Plants of Certain Regions in Jamaica, Bull. Torrey Bot. Club., 1922, **49**, 1–14, pl. 1, fig. 1.

Pessin, L. J.: An Ecological Study of the Polypody Fern, Polypodium polypodioides, an Epiphyte in Mississippi, Ecology, 1925, **6**, 17–38.

CHAPTER IX.

NUTRITIVE CONJUNCTIVE SYMBIOSIS.

CONJUNCTIVE symbiosis is said to be nutritive whenever there is a direct food relation between two or more of the symbionts. It thus includes all interrelations of a parasitic nature. By parasitic nature we mean any case in which one organism absorbs food or food materials directly from another. It obviously includes, therefore, not only the ordinary parasitic relations that we commonly call disease but also the relations existing in all gall-like structures where the gall-forming organism is parasitic on a host and often the host is in turn parasitic on the gall-forming plant or animal. Only some of the more common or otherwise interesting examples of nutritive conjunctive symbiosis can be discussed in this chapter.

63. **Antagonistic Nutritive Conjunctive Symbiosis.**—In this type of conjunctive symbiosis one or more, but not all of the symbionts derive food or food materials from other symbionts while those from which the food is taken receive no benefit but often great injury from the relationship. Ordinary parasitism as exemplified by disease, ectotrophic mycorhizas, and very many kinds of galls, belong to this type of symbiosis and will be discussed in the following paragraphs.

64. **Parasites.**—Parasites are plants or animals that derive food or food materials from other living organisms. Parasites which lack chlorophyll and so are dependent upon their hosts for all food are called holoparasites while those that have chlorophyll and thus are able to manufacture carbohydrates are called partial parasites. The latter obtain

food materials rather than food from their hosts. It is not known in most cases whether parasites, either holoparasites or partial parasites, obtain proteins from their hosts or manufacture them themselves. It is not likely that they are all alike in this respect.

Plants that obtain their food from dead organic matter are called saprophytes. These, of course, are not symbiotic, but there are many fungi and bacteria that can live equally well as parasites or as saprophytes. Such organisms are called facultative parasites. Many of the bracket fungi, such as *Polyporus sulphureus*, are of this nature. (Fig. 47.) Such a plant gets into a living tree through a wound and may live as a parasite in the tree for many years, but after the tree is dead the fungus continues to grow as a saprophyte in the dead wood. Fungi of the genus *Cordyceps*, likewise, cause diseases of certain kinds of insects. They grow as parasites in the living insects until the hosts die and then continue to live as saprophytes on the dead insect bodies. Those fungi that are obligate parasites and must have a living host in order to complete their life cycles, and yet which habitually or periodically spend a part of their lives in a non-parasitic condition, are sometimes called tropoparasites.

Familiar examples of holoparasitic seed plants are the various species of dodder (*Cuscuta*). The dodders are twining plants which lack chlorophyll and have a yellowish color. The seeds germinate on soil, usually rather late in spring after other vegetation has sprouted and young shoots of host plants are therefore available. The young shoot of a dodder is a fine, yellow, thread-like structure whose tip rotates as it elongates. If it does not come in contact with a host plant it lives but a few weeks at most. If, however, it succeeds in finding a suitable host it grows vigorously, twining about the host and at the same time penetrating it with absorbing organs, called haustoria, which in this case are modified adventitious roots. Soon the dodder loses all connection with the soil and becomes purely a holoparasite. Some species of dodder may grow on various kinds of hosts while others are restricted to a single species. Sometimes these parasites are very destructive to crops such as clover and flax.

Fig. 47.—*Daedalea confragosa*, a facultative parasite on willow.

Other important holoparasites are found in the family Orobanchaceæ, a family of root parasites. The seeds of the broom-rape (*Orobanche*) germinate only when in contact with the root of a host plant. The seedling penetrates the host at once and produces in the soil a tuber-like body. Only the flowering shoot comes above the surface of the soil. In some species the contact with the host is only at a single point which may be on a small lateral root at some distance from the main stem of the host.

The Rafflesiaceæ is a tropical family of root parasites. In the genus Rafflesia the entire vegetative part of the plant grows within the host, just as is the case with many parasitic fungi, so that the plant ordinarily is seen only when it is in flower. *Rafflesia Arnoldii,* one of these parasites, has the largest flowers that are known. They are sometimes as much as a meter in diameter.

Fig. 48.—*Arceuthobium Douglasii* (dwarf mistletoe). Pistillate plants on *Pseudotsuga mucronata.* (Photograph by James R. Weir.)

Among the most familiar partial parasites are the mistletoes; *Viscum,* the European mistletoe, *Phoradendron,* the American mistletoe, and *Arceuthobium,* the dwarf mistletoe (Figs. 48 and 49). These plants contain chlorophyll and manufacture their own carbohydrates but they are parasitic on the trunks and branches of trees and obtain water and minerals from the host plants.

The family Scrophulariaceæ contains representatives of all

9

gradations from complete independence to holoparasitism. Many of the common members of the family, as toadflax, *Linaria vulgaris,* are completely independent plants. Others, as some species of lousewort, *Pedicularis,* are mild root parasites. They contain chlorophyll and look like independent plants but they are able to augment their supply of water and minerals by robbing their neighbors. Often a

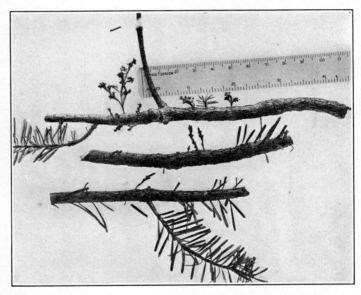

FIG. 49.—*Arceuthobium Douglasii* (dwarf mistletoe). Staminate plants on *Pseudotsuga mucronata.* (Photograph by James R. Weir.)

single plant has numerous contacts with the roots of other plants, frequently of several species at the same time. *Tozzia,* another genus of the same family, with one species occurring in the Alps and another in the Carpathians, is much different. A plant of this genus lives for two or three years in a holoparasitic, entirely subterranean, condition. It then sends up an aërial shoot which becomes green, changing the plant, therefore, to a partial parasite, and in a few weeks produces flowers and fruits and then dies. Such a life history is strikingly similar to that of a two-year cicada in the insect world. Finally, there is the European genus, *Lathraea*, also belonging to the Scrophulariaceæ, which completely lacks chlorophyll and is thus holoparasitic throughout its life.

The examples of holoparasites among the fungi and bacteria are of course innumerable, their exact relations to the host plants and the amount of injury they do being very variable. There are also various kinds of holoparasitic animals, notably several species of scale insects, that exhibit this same type of symbiotic relationship.

65. Ectotrophic Mycorhizas.—A mycorhiza, as the word suggests, is a structure composed of root and fungus. An ectotrophic mycorhiza is one in which the fungus mycelium is found on the outside of the root and between its cells, as contrasted with endotrophic mycorhizas in which the fungus occurs inside the root cells. Ectotrophic mycorhizas are found on various kinds of trees such as pines, oaks, hickories, beech, etc. They occur in the upper layers of the soil on the smallest rootlets. They usually form clusters of short, stubby branches often described as "coral branching" rootlets (Figs. 50 and 51). They vary in color from white to bright yellow, brick red, or dark brown, the color depending upon the kind of fungus.

As many as seven different kinds of fungi have been found producing mycorhizas on the same species of tree and there is probably no arbitrary limit to the number that might be so found, just as there is no arbitrary limit to the number of diseases to which a species may be subject. There is considerable evidence, however, that certain species of trees are more or less immune to the attacks of many mycorhizal fungi while other species lack such immunity.

The internal structure of the mycorhizas of dicotyledonous trees is characteristically different from that of coniferous trees. (Fig. 51.) In the case of dicotyledonous trees the cortical cells are ordinarily palisade-shaped on one side of the root and irregular in shape on the other side while such a condition has never been reported on a coniferous tree. No reason for this morphological phenomenon is known.

These mycorhizas are caused by many kinds of summer and autumn mushrooms. The mycelium of the mushroom penetrates the outer cell wall of the rootlet and splits the wall by dissolving out the middle lamella. It then continues to grow

Fig. 50.—Ectotrophic mycorhizas of the hornbeam (*Carpinus betulus*) in leaf mold. (Photograph by Somerville Hastings.)

and branch until it forms a fungus mantle which completely covers the rootlet, tip and all. At the same time branches of the mycelium penetrate between the outer cortical cells of the rootlet splitting the walls and pushing the cells apart. Further growth of the rootlet is inhibited by the fungus mantle which covers it and excessive branching is induced just as when the tip of a root or shoot is cut off. The new branches, however, are in turn transformed into mycorhizas by the mycelium, and the final result is the cluster of short stubby branches.

The ectotrophic mycorhizas of forest trees are produced during summer and autumn. They persist unchanged during the winter, so far as external appearance is concerned, and die in the spring. They are therefore annual structures. So far as the trees are concerned these mycorhizas are of little importance. The fungi are parasitic on the roots, but ordinarily the percentage of the total number of rootlets

Fig. 51.—Cross-sections of ectotrophic mycorhizas. Left from *Carya ovata;* right from *Picea rubra.*

of the tree that are affected is so small that the tree is not inconvenienced any more than when a few of its roots are broken off by a burrowing animal or some of its leaves eaten by insects.

It should be added that the view that ectotrophic mycorhizas are of little importance to trees is not held by all ecologists. Some contend that the mycorhizas are very beneficial to the trees in that the trees receive increased supplies of nitrogen through them and this contention is based upon very careful and extensive experimental evidence. On the other hand, careful microchemical tests on mycorhizas in Japan have indicated that the fungi do not supply nitrogen to the roots but that they act as ordinary parasites and take both nitrogen compounds and carbohydrates from the roots. A great deal more work will need to be done before this question can be definitely settled.

For the other symbionts, however, that is, the fungi, the mycorhizas are probably much more important. The roots of trees contain a large amount of reserve food at the time when mycorhizas are being formed and this is undoubtedly made use of by the fungi. Fungi, like all other plants, require a large amount of food for the production of their fruits. Some fungi store up the necessary supply of food, during their vegetative growth, in structures called sclerotia. The mycorhiza-forming mushrooms, however, depend upon the food in the tree roots for their fruiting activity and the mycorhizas therefore take the place of sclerotia for these fungi. In the forests of eastern and northeastern United States and of southeastern Canada mushrooms are extremely abundant and ectotrophic mycorhizas, which are also abundant, appear to be very important in the nutrition of many of the late summer and autumn mushrooms. In the central part of the Rocky Mountain region mycorhizas do not seem to play so important a part, though in some of the pacific coast regions they are probably as abundant and important as in the east.

A number of cases are known in which the mycorhizal fungus is partly ectotrophic and partly endotrophic. Such mycorhizas are said to be ectendotrophic. In most cases they probably represent merely a difference in degree of parasitism. All ectotrophic mycorhizal fungi are parasitic on the roots of the host plants. This leads to a resistance to the parasite on the part of the host cells. In most cases the fungus is able to penetrate between the cells but not to gain an entrance to them, and so remains ectotrophic. If, however, the fungus succeeds in entering the cortical cells of the root it becomes ectendotrophic. In the case of some ecten-dotrophic mycorhizas the relationship between the fungus and its host is very much in doubt. The Indian pipe (*Monotropa uniflora*) for example, is a small, colorless seed plant which was formerly thought to be a saprophyte. Usually, however, the entire root system of this plant is transformed into a cluster of ectendotrophic mycorhizas and it seems likely that the seed plant is parasitic on the fungus. If this is true, since the fungus is undoubtedly parasitic on the seed plant, the relationship is reciprocal rather than antagonistic.

66. **Galls.**—A gall is a structurally modified plant part caused by a symbiotic relation with some other organism. Usually the affected part is enlarged either through increase in size of the cells (hypertrophy) or increase in the number of cells (hyperplasy) or both. In some cases, on the other hand, there is a decrease in size through a reduction in cell size (atrophy) or a reduction in cell number (hypoplasy). Usually the plant stores up quantities of food in the tissues of the gall and these are later used by the parasitic symbiont. Partly because of these large stores of reserve materials most galls are very resistant and if a plant bearing galls is cut down, the galls often remain fresh and green long after the other parts of the plant are dead.

Galls are found on all kinds of plant parts. They are most common on stems and leaves but occur on roots, flowers, and fruits also. They exhibit a great variety of form and color, some of them being very fantastic in form and appearance, and some of them are very beautiful. They are caused by many kinds of plants and animals but chiefly by fungi and insects and more especially the latter. The kinds of insect galls are almost innumerable (Fig. 52). The great majority are produced by gall-wasps (*Cynipidæ*) or gall-gnats (*Cecidomyidæ*). Each species of insect produces galls always on the same species of plant or on a few closely-related species and, while insect galls are widely distributed in the plant kingdom, there are some groups of plants that are peculiarly susceptible. Of about 450 known gall-wasps, for example, more than 350 are found on oaks and nearly 30 on roses. The gall-gnats are somewhat less restricted than the wasps but large numbers are found upon oaks, hickories, willows, roses, legumes and composites, especially golden-rods and asters.

Fig. 52.—Insect galls on white oak.

The exact nature of the stimuli that cause the production of insect galls is not definitely known but in most cases it is probably due to mechanical irritation caused by the feeding activities of the young insects after hatching.

An interesting group of galls is that of the witches' brooms that are formed on various kinds of trees (Fig. 53). Those occurring on hackberry (*Celtis occidentalis*) are caused by mites, minute animals closely related to spiders, while most other witches' brooms are caused by fungi. The formation of a witches' broom is quite comparable to that of an ecto-trophic mycorhizal cluster. That is, the attack of the parasite on a shoot inhibits the further elongation of that shoot and causes an abnormal number of branches to be produced back of the tip. These branches are in turn attacked by the parasite and still other branches are produced the final result being a thick broom-like cluster of short branches.

Fig. 53.—Witches' broom on *Acer negundo*.

Other common galls caused by fungi are the "cedar apples" which occur on *Juniperus virginiana*, the "black knot" of plum and cherry trees, and some stem- and leaf-galls occurring on certain members of the family Ericaceæ.

The gall-causing organisms, whether plants or animals, are parasitic on the host plants, and the galls, although composed of plant tissue, are of no benefit to the plants on which they are formed. The food that is stored in the galls can never be used by the host plant, but only by the parasite. These galls then are comparable to ordinary diseases and represent antagonistic nutritive conjunctive symbiosis. Usually they are not very harmful but when they become excessively thick on a plant they are seriously detrimental.

67. **Reciprocal Nutritive Conjunctive Symbiosis.**—This type of symbiosis differs from the examples of antagonistic symbiosis discussed in the preceding paragraphs of this chapter in that all of the symbionts receive benefit from the symbiotic relation, usually in the form of food. Any organism that derives food directly from another organism is parasitic. The symbionts concerned in this type of symbiosis are, therefore, parasites and our commonest examples are those in which two unlike kinds of organisms are living together in intimate contact and each is parasitic on the other. There is thus a double or reciprocal parasitism. The examples that will be discussed in the remainder of the chapter are root and leaf tubercles caused by bacteria, endotrophic mycorhizas, and lichens.

68. **Root Tubercles.**—The best known bacterial tubercles are those found on the roots of many plants of the legume family. These tubercles are small galls, usually only a few millimeters in diameter, and are composed largely of parenchyma cells, like most other galls. Within the cells of the tubercle are found bacteria. The bacteria are facultative parasites which, in a saprophytic condition, are found rather commonly in soils. They enter the roots of leguminous plants through root hairs and become parasitic on the cells of the roots, and the roots are stimulated to produce the gall-tissues that form tubercles. At first the legume plants suffer somewhat from the presence of these parasitic bacteria but eventually many of the bacteria are digested and absorbed by the root cells.

Root tubercles are also found in the families Cycadaceæ,

Podocarpaceæ, Eleagnaceæ and Myricaceæ and in the genera *Alnus* and *Ceonothus*. In all of these cases the tubercles are produced through the modification of lateral rootlets. In this respect they differ from those of the Leguminosæ which are produced as out-growths of the cortex and not as modified lateral rootlets.

The bacteria that are concerned in the formation of these tubercles are spoken of as nitrogen-fixing bacteria because, unlike nearly all other organisms, they are able to use the uncombined nitrogen of the atmosphere, combining it with other elements to form nitrates. Nitrogen in the form of nitrate salts is readily utilized by legume plants and by other green plants. For these reasons the symbiotic relation between nitrogen-fixing bacteria and legume plants is extremely important to agriculture since it increases in the soil the available nitrates for other crop plants. It is primarily because of this symbiotic phenomenon that a legume crop is nearly always included in any rotation of crops.

69. **Leaf Tubercles.**—Some tropical plants belonging to the family Rubiaceæ, especially the genus *Pavetta*, have small galls, or tubercles, on their leaves that contain nitrogen-fixing bacteria. These bacteria seem to be very closely related to those found in the root tubercles of legume plants and their relation to the host plant is in many ways comparable. The buds of these plants always contain a jelly-like material in which some of the bacteria are present. The bacteria enter the young leaves through stomatal openings while still in the bud. They at once become parasitic and even destroy some of the leaf cells but the formation of a tubercle by the leaf tissue appears to inhibit any further encroachment of the bacteria and many of them are finally digested and absorbed by the leaf cells.

Since the bacteria are always present on the growing tips of the plant in all of its buds, they are also present in the flowers and therefore on the seeds. When a seed germinates the bacteria are thus at once present on the growing tip of the plumule. These bacteria differ from the legume bacteria, therefore, in that they spend their entire lives on and in the host plant while the legume bacteria spend a part of their lives as saprophytes in the soil.

Pavetta plants which were grown for experimental purposes from sterilized seeds and thus were free from bacteria, showed typical "nitrogen hunger." When these plants were inoculated with the bacteria they soon recovered their normal health. This indicates that the symbiotic relation has become practically obligate for both organisms since the seed plants depend upon the bacteria for their nitrogen supply and the bacteria probably cannot live at all without the host plant.

70. **Endotrophic Mycorhizas.** — Endotrophic mycorhizas are comparable to root tubercles in that there is reciprocal parasitism between the two kinds of organisms. They are caused by filamentous fungi, however, instead of bacteria, and probably few if any of these fungi are capable of fixing free nitrogen. But the fungus is parasitic on the cells of the root and the root cells finally digest and absorb the hyphæ of the fungus.

Endotrophic mycorhizas differ from ectotrophic in that the mycelium of the fungus occurs inside the cells of the root cortex rather than between the cells or on the outside of the root. In the case of the red maple, *Acer rubrum*, the rootlets containing the fungus are transformed into small bead-like galls (Fig. 54). There may be a single one of these in the case of a short rootlet or there may be several, arranged like a short string of beads, on a longer rootlet. The fungus is found only in the cortical cells of these bead-like mycorhizas. Although these mycorhizas of the maple are usually quite abundant on the roots in the superficial layers of the soil they are not thought to be of any great importance to the tree.

Among the most interesting of endotrophic mycorhizas

are those of the orchids. Many orchids are entirely dependent upon mycorhizal fungi. The seeds of some orchids will
not germinate except in the presence of the mycelium of the
mycorhizal fungus. In other species the seeds germinate
but do not develop beyond the seedling stage unless they
become infected with the proper kind of fungus. These
facts have made the propagation of orchids for commercial
purposes very difficult, and in some cases impossible, up to
the present time. The mycorhizal fungi concerned with

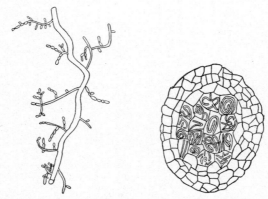

Fig. 54.—Endotrophic mycorhizas of *Acer rubrum*. Left, external appearance; right, tangential section.

most of these orchids, as well as with other endotrophic
mycorhizas, are not mushrooms but microscopic molds which
for the most part are not well known. *Gastrodia elata*, a
non-chlorophyllous orchid of Japan, however, has as its
endophyte the mycelium of *Armillaria mellea* which is a
common edible mushroom.

Recently it has been found that the seeds of certain orchids
can be germinated, and the seedlings grown, without fungi
by using a proper culture medium containing a sugar or some
other chemical which supplies the necessary stimulus. This
is the method now generally employed by florists.

Some orchids, as *Corallorhiza* and *Epipogon,* have no roots, the underground parts consisting entirely of branched rhizomes. These rhizomes always contain endophytic fungi, however, and the symbiotic relation is undoubtedly the same as in the case of orchids with roots. Such a combination of fungus and stem may be called a mycopremna.

Endotrophic mycorhizas are nearly as common in the Ericaceæ as in the Orchidaceæ, and certain genera of this family, as *Calluna, Rhododendron,* and *Vaccinium,* the blueberry, are more or less dependent upon mycorhizal fungi. These fungi can grow only in an acid medium and the blueberries and other mycorhizal plants of the Ericaceæ, therefore, can flourish only in a soil that is kept acid by some means.

In *Calluna* it has been found that the mycelium of the fungus, which belongs to the genus *Phoma,* is not only present in the roots but throughout the aërial parts of the plant as well and is always present in the seeds. The germination of these seeds seems to be as dependent upon the presence of the fungus as is that of orchid seeds.

It has recently been shown that endotrophic mycorhizas are abundant in the composite and legume families and probably in some others but nothing is known of their significance in these families. The fungi in the mycorhizas of these families appear to belong to the group known as Phycomycetes but none of them have ever been isolated for identification.

71. **Lichens.**—A lichen is a symbiotic combination of fungus mycelium and one-celled algæ (Fig. 55). It used to be thought that lichens were single unit organisms and they were classified along with the liverworts. The green cells in them, which are now known to be algæ, were called gonidia. The fact that the lichen is a plant complex rather than a single organism was discovered by growing the fungi and algæ separately. Later lichens were synthesized by placing lichen fungi among algæ that had been growing free in nature. In these cases the mycelium enveloped some of

the algal cells and lichens of the usual kind resulted. The algæ that are concerned in lichens commonly belong to a few well-known genera such as *Pleurococcus* and *Nostoc*. The fungi, however, appear to have been greatly modified by the symbiotic relation since they are very different from any fungi known outside of lichens.

Fig. 55.—Lichens on rock.   (Photograph by Bruce Fink.)

Although lichens are dual organisms, that is they are made up of two distinct kinds of plants, yet they exhibit a high degree of unity and in many respects behave as single organisms. Perhaps the most striking indication of a high degree of unity is seen in the bodies called soredia. A soredium is a vegetative reproductive body consisting of a small amount of fungus tissue enclosing a few algal cells. It is the commonest and most efficient method of reproduction that a lichen has. The lichen fungi, of course, produce spores but these spores can never develop into lichens unless they chance to fall among algæ of a suitable species. The efficiency of the soredium, therefore, is due to the fact that it keeps the two symbionts together. It is practically the only case known in which two symbionts have a common reproductive body.

Another feature that makes lichens seem like unit organisms is the fact that they are able to grow in extremely dry situations. Fungi, as a group, are characteristically plants of medium conditions with respect to water supply, while algæ as a group, are characteristically plants of very wet situations, many of them growing in water. But, when fungi and algæ live together in the intimate symbiotic relationship under discussion, the resulting organisms are more resistant to dry conditions than any other group of plants. It is for this reason that lichens form the outposts of the plant world in nearly every direction. In going toward the poles the last plants one sees are pretty certain to be lichens. At the tops of the highest mountains the plants are almost exclusively lichens. At the tops of tall tropical trees, if any plants are found growing as epiphylls on the leaves that are fully exposed to the hot tropical sun, they are lichens.

The exact physiological relationship between the two components of a lichen is still very imperfectly known although it has been studied and discussed for a very long time. Some writers have thought that a lichen represents a sort of partnership between the fungus and the algæ each partner supplying to the other certain necessities of life. Others have taken a somewhat opposite view and have believed the algæ to have been enslaved by the fungus. Still others have considered the fungus as an ordinary parasite on the algæ, or have said that the fungus is diseased by the algæ. It is improbable that the physiological relationship between lichen-fungus and alga is the same in all cases. It is reasonably certain, however, that in the majority of lichens the fungus obtains organic food from the algæ, either as a parasite on the living gonidia or as a saprophyte on dead ones. Similarly, it is certain that the algæ obtain water, at least, from the fungus, either directly or indirectly. The relationship has apparently reached such a balance that it is more or less normal for both fungus and alga, and both can endure it, therefore, without suffering. This, however, must not be taken to imply a sort of reciprocity agreement under which each party supplies something to the other. Rather each party takes all it can get from the other. In other words the lichen represents a case of double, or reciprocal, parasitism, and must be classified as reciprocal nutritive conjunctive symbiosis.

REFERENCES.

Cosens, A.: A Contribution to the Morphology and Biology of Insect Galls, Trans. Canadian Inst., 1913, **9**, 297–387.

Darbishire, O. V.: Some Aspects of Lichenology, Trans. British Mycol. Soc., 1924, **10**, 10–27.

Fagan, M. M.: The Uses of Insect Galls, Am. Nat., 1918, **52**, 155–176.

Felt, E. P.: Gall-insects and their Relation to Plants, Scientific Monthly, 1918, **16**, 509–525.

Fink, Bruce: The Rate of Growth and Ecesis in Lichens, Mycologia, 1917, **9**, 138–158.

Fry, E. Jennie: The Mechanical Action of Corticolous Lichens, Ann. Bot., 1926, 4(**158**), 397–417.

Herbert, A.: The Root Parasitism of Western Australian Santalaceæ, Jour. and Proc. Roy. Soc. Western Australia, 1925, **11**, 127–149.

Knudson, Lewis: Physiological Study of the Symbiotic Germination of Orchid Seeds, Bot. Gaz., 1925, **79**, 345–379.

MacDougal, D. T.: The Making of Parasites, Plant World, 1910, **13**, 207–214.

McDougall, W. B.: On the Mycorhizas of Forest Trees, Am. Jour. Bot., 1914, **1**, 51–74.

McDougall, W. B.: Mycorhizas of Coniferous Trees, Jour. Forestry, 1922, **20**, 255–260.

McDougall, W. B.: Mycorhizas from North Carolina and Eastern Tennessee, Am. Jour. Bot., 1928, **15**, 141–148.

McDougall, W. B. and Glasgow, Olalla: Mycorhizas of the Compositæ, Am. Jour. Bot., 1929, **16**, 225–228.

McDougall, W. B. and Jacobs, Margaret C.: Tree Mycorhizas from the Central Rocky Mountain Region, Am. Jour. Bot., 1927, **14**, 258–266.

McLuckie, John: Studies in Symbiosis, Proc. Linn. Soc., New South Wales, 1922, **47**, 293–310, 319–328.

McLuckie, John: Studies in Symbiosis, Proc. Linn. Soc., New South Wales, 1922, **47**, 293–310, 319–328.

McLuckie, John: Studies in Parasitism: A Contribution to the Physiology of the Loranthaceæ of New South Wales, Bot. Gaz., 1923, **75**, 333–369.

Masui, Haki: A Study of the Mycorhiza of *Abies firma* S. et Z., with Special Reference to its Mycorhizal Fungus, *Cantharellus floccosus*, Schum., Mem. Coll. Sci. Kyoto Imp. Univ., 1926, Ser. B2 (1), 15–84.

Maybrook, A. C.:   On the Haustoria of Pedicularis Vulgaris Tournef, Ann. Bot., 1917, **31**, 499–512.

Paulson, Robert and Hastings, Somerville: The Relation between Alga and Fungus of a Lichen, Jour. Linn. Soc. Bot., 1920, **44**, 497–506.

Ramsbottom, J.:   Orchid Mycorrhiza, Trans. British Mycol. Soc., 1922, **8**, 28–61.

Rayner, M. Cheveley: Mycorrhiza in the Ericaceæ, Trans. British Mycol. Soc., 1922, **8**, 61–66.

Rayner, M. Cheveley: Nitrogen-fixation in Ericaceæ, Bot. Gaz., 1922, **73**, 226–235.

Rayner, M. Cheveley: The Nutrition of Mycorrhiza Plants, British Jour. Exp. Biol., 1925, **2**, 265–292.

Rayner, M. C.:   Mycorrhiza, Wheldon and Wesley, London, 1927.

Smith, A. Loraine: Recent Work on Lichens, Trans. British Mycol. Soc., 1925, **10**, 133–152.

Spratt, Ethel R.:   The Root Nodules of the Cycadaceæ, Ann. Bot., 1915, **27**, 619–626.

Spratt, Ethel R.:   A Comparative Account of the Root-nodules of the Leguminosæ, Ann. Bot., 1919, **33**, 189–199.

Stewart, Alban: A Consideration of Certain Pathological Conditions in Ambrosia Trifida, Am. Jour. Bot., 1919, **6**, 34–46.

CHAPTER X.

PHYSICAL FACTORS: LIGHT.

ANY part of the environment of a plant that affects in any way the life of the plant may be spoken of as an environmental factor or ecological factor. The environment of any plant is partly living and partly non-living. The living part of the environment consists of plants and animals. These may be spoken of collectively as biotic factors. They have been discussed at some length in the chapters on Symbiosis and will be dealt with further in some of the succeeding chapters.

The non-living part of the environment consists of a variety of influences that may be spoken of collectively as physical factors. The more important of these will be discussed in the present and the immediately following chapters.

72. **Gravity.**—An environmental factor becomes important ecologically as it varies from place to place and in its effect upon different kinds of plants. If all factors produced the same effects on all plants everywhere there would be no science of ecology, just as there would be no science of human sociology if the environmental conditions in which human beings live were universally the same.

Gravity is the one universal factor. Its action is practically the same on all parts of the earth's surface. Since it is a universal factor it is not of very great importance ecologically, though it is very important physiologically. Generally speaking the effect of gravity is to cause roots to grow downward and stems to grow upward, but it is a curious fact that the directions of growth of the lateral roots and the lateral shoots are also directed largely by gravity. The advantage of this phenomenon is, of course, clear enough, since it would be a distinct disadvantage to a plant to have all its roots grow straight downward and all its stems straight upward. As long as the main shoot and the main root are intact the lateral branches seem to be inhibited from growing straight upward or straight downward, since if the main shoot is cut off one or more of the stronger lateral branches will then assume the vertical direction. This whole phenomenon is still very imperfectly understood and may not be due entirely to gravity.

The effect of gravity on the lower plants is comparable to that on seed plants. For example, the orientation of the fruit-bodies of fungi is due, for the most part, to gravity. In the case of the toad-stool type of mushroom, with gills on the under side of the cap, the spores cannot be shed unless the cap is horizontal and the gills vertical. When such a mushroom grows from the side of a stump or log, the stem, through a response to gravity, always curves in such a way as to bring the cap into a horizontal position (Fig. 56).

73. **Light.**—Light is not, like gravity, a universal factor. The amount of light in different places and at different times varies greatly. The source of all light is the sun, and the amount of light received by any place on the surface of the earth depends upon the length of the day and the angle at which the sun shines. At the time of the spring equinox in March and again at the fall equinox in September the day is twelve hours long everywhere on the surface of the earth. But at all other times the days are twelve hours long only at the equator and become either longer or shorter as one goes toward either pole. The intensity of light also varies greatly as the season advances because of the changing angle at which the sun shines, being most intense where the incident rays of light are most nearly vertical.

The intensity of light is also greatly affected by the condition of the weather as everyone who has done photographic work well knows. The merest film of cloud in front of the sun brings about an appreciable reduction in the light intensity and the effect of thicker clouds is of course much greater. There are thus three variables that change the amount and intensity of light in any given place; namely, the time of year, the time of day, and the condition of the weather.

The quality of light is also an important factor. A beam of white light consists of many rays which differ in length

Fig. 56.—Clusters of mushrooms (*Collybia velutipes*) that grew on the lower side of a horizontal tree trunk. The curved stems are due to a response to gravity.

and which, when separated, form the series of colors that are characteristic of a rainbow or a spectrum. The colors run in order through shades of red, orange, yellow, green, blue, indigo, and violet. Beyond the violet are the ultra-violet rays which are invisible to the human eye but which produce certain effects upon plants. These ultra-violet rays have very short wave lengths while the red rays have the longest wave lengths. The rays with long wave lengths, that is those at the red end of the spectrum, are the ones most used by the plant in the manufacture of carbohydrates. On the other hand the shorter wave lengths, violet and ultra-violet, are most important in checking vegetative growth. Since these short wave lengths are more readily absorbed by atmosphere, and especially by clouds, than the longer ones, the quality of the light varies greatly between high and low altitudes and between clear and cloudy weather.

74. **The Effect of Length of Day.**—At the equator the days are always twelve hours long and during the summer of either hemisphere the length of the days increase toward the pole until at the pole light is continuous throughout the summer. The long days of the north, during the summer of the northern hemisphere, enable plants to develop rapidly and mature quickly. It is largely because of the longer days that oranges are ripe and ready for the market several weeks earlier in the northern part of the Central Valley of California than they are 400 miles farther south. It is also primarily due to the long periods of sunshine during the growing season that large crops of hay, wheat, potatoes, and other vegetables can be grown in some parts of Alaska.

Experiments have shown that some seed plants normally produce flowers only when the days are relatively long and so may be spoken of as long-day plants. Others come into bloom only when the days are relatively short and are called short-day plants. Long-day plants, such as evening primrose, red clover and radish, can be made to bloom earlier than they normally would by lengthening the day by means of artificial light.

Short-day plants, on the other hand, such as tobacco, dahlia and ragweed respond in just the opposite way from the long-day plants and, therefore, in order to bring them into bloom earlier it is necessary to shorten the period of illumination by placing the plants in a dark place during a part of each day. It seems likely that many of the periodic phenomena of plants are controlled largely by the relative length of day and night, and that they may be greatly modified by increasing or decreasing the daily period of illumination. These facts are of especial importance to florists and others engaged in growing plants in greenhouses since they indicate that it may be possible to produce flowers and fruits earlier or later than the usual season (Figs. 57, 58 and 59).

75. The Requirement of Light by Plants.—There is no place in the world where there is not enough light for plant life.

Fig. 57.—*Aster linariifolius* L.   Plants in box on left exposed to light from 9 a.m. to 4 p.m. daily.   In full bloom when photographed June 21. Plants in box on right left out of doors during the test.   Showed no indications of flower heads when photographed June 24.   (After Garner and Allard.)

Even in the depths of the ocean and in underground caves there are saprophytic bacteria and molds that bring about the decay of any organic matter that may be there.   Some of these saprophytic plants can spend their entire lives in total darkness and some of them are readily killed by exposure to light.   All green plants, however, require a certain

Fig. 58.—Wild lettuce. (*Lactuca spicata*). Plants at left, exposed to a ten-hour day beginning March 29, produced much larger, coarser leaves than the control plants (at right) exposed to the full summer length of day. Under the short-day exposure both leaf and stem were far more hairy than under the long-day conditions. The stature was greatly reduced, but the time of flowering was not affected. (After Garner and Allard.)

amount of light. Chlorophyll, except in a few cases, is formed only in light, and it cannot function for carbohydrate synthesis without light. Many saprophytic and parasitic

FIG. 59.—*Oenothera biennis.* Plants at left were exposed to the full day-light period of the spring months. The individual at right received only ten hours of illumination beginning March 19. It is seen that the short-day conditions caused a decided weakening in power to elongate the primary axis, resulting in development of numerous basal shoots. In this case domi-nance of the apical bud is lost, a characteristic response to a suboptimal light period for elongation of the stem. Photographed June 21. (After Garner and Allard.)

fungi which can flourish vegetatively in the dark require light at the time of fruiting.

Most plants actually use only a small part of the light that they receive. Many of them could probably get along with

less than 1 per cent of the light that is normally available
for them.   Yet there is for each species an optimum amount
as well as an upper zero point or maximum and a lower zero
point or minimum.   In general, low intensities of light favor
the growth of vegetative structures. The largest leaves
and the fullest development of many kinds of stems are found
in partial shade.   Many vegetative crops, such as potatoes,
beets, carrots and turnips, yield best in regions where there
is a high percentage of cloudy days.   Ginseng, when grown
commercially, is covered with slat frames so that it will not
be fully exposed to the light, and tea is usually planted in
alternate rows with taller trees, the shade causing the tea
leaves to become large and of good quality.

On the other hand, intense light favors the development of
flowers, fruits, and seeds.   The best regions in which to grow
fruits and grains, therefore, are those in which there is a
high percentage of bright, sunny days, provided there is also
a sufficient amount of moisture.   Furthermore, the brightest
colors and the greatest profusion of flowers are found in
Arctic meadows where the light is very intense, while in the
shade of a dense forest flowers are scarce.

The seedlings of many trees are unable to grow in the shade
of other trees.   Such trees are said to be intolerant; that is,
they are intolerant of shade.   Other trees are spoken of as
tolerant because they can get along very well, during their
seedling stages, in the shade of other trees.   This difference
between species becomes very important when tolerant
and intolerant trees are growing together in a forest.   The
seeds of both may germinate but only seedlings of the tolerant
kinds can continue to grow.   Whenever any of the old trees
die or fall, therefore, their places are certain to be taken by
tolerant trees.   The obvious result of this is that finally
the forest comes to be composed of tolerant trees only.
Though light is not the only factor concerned in tolerance
it is an extremely important one.   The phenomena of
tolerance and intolerance are of great significance in connec-

tion with the development of plant communities to be discussed in later chapters.

76. Adaptations for Securing Light.—Plants are adapted in various ways for procuring the necessary amount of light. Our early spring flowers which live in forests, for example, carry on those activities that require an abundance of light before the trees have leaved. Many of them are active only about three months and, becoming dormant soon after the leaves of the trees are out, remain so until the following spring. The habits of twining plants and of other climbers are significant primarily because they serve to bring the foliage into such positions that it may be displayed to the light.

The foliage of many plants has a mosaic arrangement, often called a leaf mosaic, in which the leaves are arranged in such a way that there is a minimum of overlapping, consecutive leaves never being directly above one another. In many trees the branches are progressively longer from the top toward the base so that the leaves, which occur only near the outer extremities, are not shaded by the leaves of higher branches. This is especially true of coniferous trees which are often nearly perfectly cone-shaped but it is more or less true of many other trees and also of many herbaceous plants. When trees grow close together as in a forest the lower branches which receive insufficient light soon die and drop off (Fig. 60). Such trees are no longer cone-shaped, but their leaves are produced only near the top and so are all well exposed.

Some kinds of leaves are much more sensitive to light than other kinds. Leaves that are not very sensitive to light, as those of the tulip tree, *Liriodendron tulipifera*, are apt to assume a great variety of positions with respect to light, but those that are more sensitive, as those of the sugar maple, *Acer saccharum*, practically always have their blades at right angles to the direction from which they receive the greatest light, their petioles being twisted in such a way as to bring this about. Some plants, as the common mallow,

Malva rotundifolia, have leaves that are so sensitive to light that their blades turn toward the east in the morning and follow the sun toward the west during the day, keeping the broad face always at right angles to the source of light.

Fig. 60.—A larch tree the branches of which have been mostly self-pruned from the side toward the forest but not from the side toward the street. A light relation.

77. Protection from Excessive Light.—Although all green plants must have a certain amount of light, that which is very intense may disintegrate chlorophyll. Most plants are able to protect themselves from such a calamity by moving the chloroplasts out of the direct light. That is, if a plant remains in direct sunlight for a time, its chloroplasts are usually found to be arranged mostly along the walls that are perpendicular to the leaf surface, where they are somewhat protected from the light rays. On the other hand, if the same plant is exposed to dim light, its chloroplasts gradually assume positions mostly along the walls that are parallel to the surface, where they receive as much light as possible. One of the filamentous algæ, *Mougeotia*, shows somewhat comparable chloroplast movements. In this alga there is a single large chloroplast in the shape of a rectangular plate in each cell. When this alga is in diffuse light the chloroplasts present their broad faces to the incident rays of light but when in bright light they turn so that the edge of the plate is toward the light.

Certain plants, especially *Lactuca scariola*, the prickly lettuce, and *Silphium laciniatum*, the rosin weed, are called compass plants because most of their leaves are edgewise and in a north and south plane. This condition holds, however, only for plants growing in full sunlight, the leaves of the same species growing in partial shade being horizontal. It is fairly certain, therefore, that the vertical position of the leaves of compass plants is a result of light conditions. It is probable that this position protects the chloroplasts from too great an intensity of light, since the sun's rays are perpendicular to the flat side of the leaves only in the morning and the evening when the light is much less intense than during the middle of the day.

A similar protection is had by such plants as *Iris*, *Typha*, and many grasses, the leaves of which are vertical. The position of such leaves, however, is probably not a response to light conditions entirely since they are held in position by their sheathing bases, and probably a greater advantage than that of protection from intense light is that light is permitted to penetrate nearly or quite to the bases of the leaves. This enables the entire length of the leaf to be utilized for photosynthetic activity.

78. Measurement of Light.—Measurements of light are usually relative rather than absolute, that is, the result of such measurements are expressed in units which represent, not the absolute amount of light, but the amount as compared to some other amount which is used as a standard. The method that has been used more than any other is the tinting of silver chloride paper ("printing out" paper) to a standard tint and noting the time required to reach that tint. The chief objection to this method is that the silver chloride paper is not sensitive to the longer wave lengths of light, the ones most used in photosynthesis. For making comparisons between different habitats, however, the method has considerable value.

The Clements photometer is the instrument that is most used in light measurements by the silver chloride method. This consists of a circular metal box around which a strip of "printing out" paper may be fastened. The "cover" is slipped on outside of the paper and fastened at the center by a thumb-screw in such a way that it may be revolved. The cover has an opening at one side which is closed by a shutter. When an exposure is to be made the shutter is withdrawn for a definite length of time as measured by a stop-watch and the cover is then revolved one unit-space in preparation for the next exposure. Twenty-five exposures may be made with one strip of paper. The paper is later removed from the instrument in diffuse light and compared to a strip of standard tints.

The Macbeth illuminometer is an instrument in which the "brightness of field" produced by the light to be measured is compared to that produced by a Mazda lamp, the lamp being adjustable as to distance. It has lately come into use and has received favorable comment from a number of ecologists. Several other types of instruments have been devised and tried with varying degrees of success, but the whole field of light measurement is still in the experimental stage and no photometer yet devised is entirely satisfactory.

REFERENCES.

Adams, J.: The Effect on Certain Plants of Altering the Daily Period of Light, Ann. Bot., 1923, **37**, 75–94.

Adams, J.: Some Further Experiments on the Relation of Light to Growth, Am. Jour. Bot., 1925, **12**, 398–412.

Atkins, W. R. G. and Poole, H. H.: Photoelectric Measurements of Illumination in Relation to Plant Distribution, Part I, Sci. Proc. Roy. Dublin Soc., 1926, **18**, 277–298.

Braid, K. W.: The Measurement of Light for Ecological Purposes, Jour. Ecology, 1923, **11**, 49–63.

Burns, George P.: Measurement of Solar Radiant Energy in Plant Habitats, Ecology, 1923, **4**, 189–195, fig. 1–3.

Garner, W. W. and Allard, H. A.: Effect of the Relative Length of Day and Night and Other Factors of the Environment on Growth and Reproduction in Plants, Jour. Agr. Res., 1920, **18**, 553–606, 3 fig., pl. 64–79.

Garner, W. W. and Allard, H. A.: Further Studies in Photoperiodism, the Response of the Plant to Relative Length of Day and Night, Jour. Agr. Res., 1923, **23**, 871–920, pl. 1–19.

Gilbert, Basil E.: Interrelation of Relative Day Length and Temperature, Bot. Gaz., 1926, **81**, 1–24.

Klugh, A. Brooker: A Comparison of Certain Methods of Measuring Light for Ecological Purposes, Ecology, 1927, **8**, 415–427.

Klugh, A. Brooker: Ecological Photometry and a New Instrument for Measuring Light, Ecology, 1925, **6**, 203–235, 1 pl., 5 fig.

McCrea, R. H.: Light Intensity Measurement by Means of Hydriodic Acid, Jour. Ecology, 1923, **11**, 103–112, 3 fig.

Schaffner, J. H.: The Influence of Relative Length of Daylight on the Reversal of Sex in Hemp, Ecology, 1923, **4**, 323–334, 3 fig.

Shelford, Victor E. and Gail, Floyd W.: A Study of Light Penetration into Sea Water Made with a Kunz Photo-electric Cell, with Particular Reference to the Distribution of Plants, Publ. Puget Sound Biol., Sta. 1922, **3**, 141–176.

CHAPTER XI.

HEAT.

HEAT is a factor that is of very great importance to plants but one that is difficult to study in such a way as to yield tangible results. There seems to be little, if any, relation between structure and temperature. For this reason we cannot readily see the effect of heat or lack of heat upon the plant, and it is very difficult to separate heat as a factor from other factors that are acting at the same time. There are many structural features of plants that were formerly attributed to heat that are really due, for the most part at least, to other factors.

Plants may be compared, in a sense, to cold-blooded animals. Their internal temperatures vary with the external temperature and their greatest activity takes place at an optimum temperature, while at very low or very high temperatures they are sluggish or dormant. Each species of plant has a maximum temperature and a minimum temperature beyond which activity ceases, as well as an optimum temperature at which it is most active.

79. **Minimum Temperatures.**—In general plants are adapted to temperatures ranging from 0° to 100° C. The reason for setting these rather arbitrary limits is simply that plants, in order to carry on their functions, must have liquid water, and, of course, water ordinarily solidifies at 0° and vaporizes at 100° C. There are a few of the lower plants, however, that are active at temperatures below zero. Some of the algæ that occur in Arctic waters appear to be active at temperatures below zero. The water in which they live is still liquid, however, since there is salt enough in the water to lower the freezing-point several degrees below zero.

The "black spot" fungus which is found on meat in cold storage is able to grow and even produce spores at temperatures as low as 6° below zero. This growth is not luxuriant, of course, and very little water is required.

Plants apparently have no protection against low temperatures. Their internal temperature rises and falls with the external temperature. To be sure, heat is liberated by respiration within the plant as in an animal, but the plant cannot keep up its internal temperature by respiration, as a warm-blooded animal can, because the optimum temperature for respiration is rather high and the rate of respiration decreases with a lowering of the temperature. Therefore, when the plant most needs extra heat it cannot supply it through respiration. The internal temperature of the plant often is somewhat higher than the external temperature during the day. The internal temperature of pine leaves, for example, has been found to be from 2° to 10° higher than that of the surrounding air during the day. This, however, has been attributed to the absorption of radiant energy rather than to respiration.

The death of plants by winter-killing, or from cold at any time, is very frequently the result of desiccation rather than directly from low temperature. Thus, plants that are protected from drying winds can endure much lower temperatures than those of the same species that are fully exposed. There is no place in the world that is too cold for plant life. There are, however, places that are too continuously cold. Many plants, when in a dormant condition, can live for a considerable time at temperatures far below zero, but they cannot grow and reproduce in such temperatures. It is not known for many plants what the minimum temperature beyond which life ceases is. It varies greatly at different times of the year and with different conditions of the plant, especially as to the amount of moisture present in the plant.

For some plants temperatures below zero are necessary periodically. Some seeds, for example, will not germinate

11

until they have been subjected to freezing temperatures and this is true also of the spores of some fungi.

80. Maximum Temperatures.—No plants are active at temperatures of 90° C. or higher. The maximum temperatures that can be endured, however, like the minimum temperatures, vary greatly with different species of plants and with different internal and external conditions. Certain species of yeast have been shown to be capable of enduring a temperature of 114° C. when in a dormant condition. Many very dry seeds can endure temperatures above 100° C. while the same species in an active state would be killed by a much lower temperature. Certain algæ found in hot springs live and carry on their various functions at 77° C. and there are a few fungi which can endure as much as 89° C. Some lichens, and perhaps even seed plants, that live in tropical deserts, where the air temperatures, and more especially the surface soil temperatures, become exceedingly hot, must endure temperatures of 70° C. or higher frequently.

Most of the plants we are familiar with, however, live where the temperature never goes much beyond 40° C. and if subjected to higher temperatures when in an active condition, since they cannot quickly go into a dormant state, they suffer death.

81. Optimum Temperatures.—The optimum temperature for any plant is the temperature at which the plant gets along best in the conditions under which it is living. There is an optimum temperature for each physiological function of the plant and these various optima, for the most part, do not coincide. The ecological optimum is thus a temperature at which the plant as a whole is most nearly in harmony with the environment and it may not coincide with a single one of the physiological optima. The ecological optimum varies greatly for different plants and for the same plant at different ages and at different times during the year or even at different times of day. For example, the optimum temperature during the day, at least for plants of temperate climates, is always higher than that for the night. For many plants the optimum temperature becomes progressively higher from the time of germination to the time of fruiting, though it must be admitted that we have accurate knowledge of these variations for only a very few plants. Probably no plant, in its natural environment, ever enjoys its ecological optimum of temperature throughout an entire year. However, a plant may be said to be successful if it can reproduce each year, and plants vary so greatly in their adaptations to heat as well as to other factors that they are found to flourish under extreme conditions. Some Arctic and Alpine plants produce their flowers while the ground is still partly covered with snow and continue to flourish even though the temperature goes below freezing each night, while some tropical species carry on their activities at temperatures so high that many plants, if subjected to them, would perish in a very short time. Some plants, such as certain trees, can endure a very wide range of temperature, while others, especially some algæ, are active only within a very narrow and very definite range of temperature.

82. **Soil Temperatures.**—The temperature of the soil is very important to the plant largely because of its effect upon the rate of absorption of water. Seeds cannot germinate until the soil has been warmed up to a certain temperature, depending upon the species, nor can perennial plants become active in spring until the soil is sufficiently warm so that water can be absorbed readily by the roots.

Soil temperatures vary greatly in different situations. The soil of a bottomland is usually considerably cooler than that of the adjacent upland, particularly if the two are supporting comparable types of vegetation. The soil of a south-facing slope warms up much more rapidly in spring than does a north-facing slope and therefore, dandelions, hepaticas, and other spring flowers bloom earlier on a south-facing slope than elsewhere.

Soil temperature depends in part on the color of the soil

surface. A dark-colored soil absorbs heat and so warms up more rapidly than a light-colored soil which reflects the heat rays. A cold soil can be warmed to a certain extent by spreading over the surface a layer of dark-colored soil. The soil temperature also depends to a certain extent upon the water content, a wet soil being colder than a drier one of similar type, and one result of drainage, though not the most important one, is the increase in temperature through a decrease in water content.

83. Temperature and Plant Distribution.—The distribution of plants is governed to a certain extent by temperature. Thus, broad belts of vegetation may be recognized between the equator and the poles extending parallel with the equator and corresponding roughly to temperature belts. One also encounters somewhat similar belts in going up a mountain and the corresponding belts are usually somewhat lower on the south side of the mountain than on the north side, because of the difference in temperature. The kind of vegetation, however, is not so much affected by temperature as is the flora. By the flora of a region we mean the species of plants that occur there, while the kind of vegetation refers to the general type, such as forest, grassland, or desert. For example, we find forests in every one of the great temperature zones of the earth but the species of trees that make up the forests are different in each zone. The relation of temperature to floral distribution is well expressed by what we may call Schimper's First Law. This states that "The type of the flora in so far as it depends on existing factors is determined primarily by heat."

84. Temperature and Crop Plants.—While we must not make the mistake of over-emphasizing temperature as a controlling factor in the distribution of crop plants, yet it is to be expected that Schimper's First Law applies to specific crop plants to the same extent that it does to uncultivated species except as its action is modified or prevented by man. A definite amount of heat is required to mature each crop and various attempts have been made to find an approximate measure of this amount of heat. There is for each crop plant, as well as for every other kind of plant, a minimum temperature at which activity begins. Any temperatures below this minimum are entirely ineffective in advancing the crop toward maturity. Therefore, there must be a considerable number of days during which the temperature rises above the minimum if the plants are to mature.

A summation of the day-degrees of temperature in excess of the minimum from the date of planting to the date of maturity is known as the "thermal constant" and may be used as an approximate measure of the heat required to mature the crop. For example, if 40° F. be taken as the minimum effective temperature, then any day on which the temperature reached 50° F. would count as ten day-degrees, one on which the temperature reached 54° F. would count as fourteen day-degrees, and so on. The thermal constant would then be found by adding together all of these excess day-degrees for the season during which the crop was developing and maturing. Such thermal constants are of considerable practical value since they enable one to determine whether a given locality is favorable for the maturing of a given crop. If the climate of the locality is such that the necessary number of excess day-degrees to make up the thermal constant for the crop under consideration cannot be expected, then it is useless to attempt to grow such a crop in that locality.

In deriving the thermal constant the minimum effective temperature has often been chosen arbitrarily and the same one used for all crop plants. Such a method is obviously unsuitable since the minimum temperature for germination, or for any other activity, varies greatly with different species of plants. A somewhat more satisfactory method is to use as the minimum effective temperature the mean daily temperature at planting time since the two may be shown to approximately correspond. Farmers ordinarily plant each crop at about the same time each year without much reference to any thermometer, but they have, quite unknowingly, hit upon dates that correspond to the minimum temperatures of which we are speaking. Therefore, by noting the average time of planting each crop for a long series of years it is readily possible to determine the mean daily temperature at planting time, and this has been done for a number of crops.

By using the above method it has been found that the planting of spring wheat begins when the temperature has risen to about 37° F., spring oats are planted when the temperature is at 43° F., early potatoes at 45° F., corn at 55° F. and cotton at 62° F. The temperature for the planting of each crop is fairly uniform wherever the crop is grown. For example, early potatoes are planted in some of the southern states as early as the middle of February while in some of the northern states planting does not begin until about May 1, but in each locality the planting begins when the mean daily temperature has risen to about 45° F.

The thermal constants have not been actually worked out for many plants but they could readily be computed from data that have been accumulated by the United States Department of Agriculture and the United States Weather Bureau. The thermal constant for corn computed from the mean daily temperature at the average date of planting to the beginning of harvest is about 1600° to 1800° F., depending on the variety of corn grown, in the principal corn-producing regions. The thermal constant for cotton is about 1900° F. and temperature is the principal limiting factor in determining the northern limit of successful commercial production of cotton. If a variety of cotton could be developed which would mature with a few hundred day-degrees of temperature less than 1900 the area of cotton production in the United States could be very greatly extended.

85. **Fire.**—Fire produces very high temperatures for short periods of time in very local areas. Its most common effect is the destruction of vegetation. The greatest losses from

fires occur in forest regions where hundreds of acres of valuable timber are destroyed each year (Fig. 61). Forest fires are started by various agencies. Fires are left unextinguished by campers, or smokers throw away burning matches or cigarette stubs, but many fires are also started by electrical storms.

In addition to the destruction of vegetation there are various other effects that may be produced by fire. The

FIG. 61.—A "cemetery" forest of Engleman spruce. Killed by fire.

seed-bearing cones of the lodge pole pine (*Pinus Murrayana*) often remain closed and hang on the tree for years. The heat from a forest fire, however, will frequently cause these cones to open up and allow the seeds to fall. This phenomenon is often a deciding factor in determining the type of reproduction on a burned-over forest area. In forests where the humus layer is deep and very dry, fire may destroy the entire layer of organic matter and may thus convert a dry forest into a swamp or shallow lake. Recent studies have indicated that in some grasslands the vegetative growth of the grasses is stimulated rather than injured by periodic burning.

REFERENCES.

Burkholder, Walter H.: The Effect of Two Soil Temperatures on the Yield and Water Relations of Healthy and Diseased Bean Plants, Ecology, 1920, **1**, 113–123.

Buxton, P. A.: The Temperature of the Surface of Deserts, Jour. Ecology, 1924, **12**, 127–134.

Dickson, James G.: Influence of Soil Temperature on the Development of the Seedling Blight of Wheat and Corn Caused by Giberella Saubinettii, Jour. Agr. Res., 1923, **23**, 837–870, pl. 1–6 (1 and 2 colored), fig. 1–15.

Hartzell, F. Z.: Comparison of Methods for Computing Daily Mean Temperatures; Effect of Discrepancies upon Investigations of Climatologists and Biologists, New York Agr. Exp. Sta. (Geneva) Tech. Bull., 1919, **68**, 1–35, pl. 1–2, fig. 1–19.

Hensel, R. L.: Recent Studies on the Effect of Burning on Grassland Vegetation, Ecology, 1923, **4**, 183–188.

Kincer, J. B.: The Relation of Climate to the Geographic Distribution of Crops in the United States, Ecology, 1922, **3**, 127–133.

Larson, J. A.: Natural Reproduction After Fires in Northern Idaho, Jour. Agric. Res., 1925, **30**, 1177–1197.

Lovejoy, P. S.: The Effect of Forest Fires upon the Soil of the Northern Lake States, Rept. Michigan Acad. Sci., 1920, **22**, 9–20.

McDougall, W. B.: A Comparison of Soil Temperatures in Upland and Bottomland Forests, Trans. Illinois Acad. Sci., 1920, **13**, 249–254, 2 figs.

Miller, Edwin C. and Saunders, A. R.: Some Observations on the Temperature of the Leaves of Crop Plants, Jour. Agr. Res., 1923, **26**, 15–43. 8 fig.

Seeley, Dewey Alsdorf: The Relation Between Temperature and Crops, Rept. Michigan Acad. Sci., 1917, **19**, 167–196.

Shreve, Forrest: Soil Temperature as Influenced by Altitude and Slope Exposure, Ecology, 1924, **5**, 128–136, fig. 1–6.

Toumey, J. W. and Neethling, E. J.: Insolation, a Factor in the Natural Regeneration of Certain Conifers, Yale Univ. School Forest. Bull., 1924, **11**, 1–61, pl. 1–2, fig. 1–18.

CHAPTER XII.

AIR.

ALL plants need air for respiration and green plants need it also for photosynthesis. Air in many of its relations to plants is nearly as universal as gravity. We shall not deal with it, therefore, in many of its physiological relations but only in those relations that are variable enough to be of ecological significance.

86. **Atmospheric Composition and Pressure.**—The composition of the atmosphere does not vary materially from place to place except in the amount of dust and smoke that it contains. In large cities there is often enough dust or smoke, or both, in the air to exclude certain kinds of plants entirely. Most evergreen trees, for example, are unable to endure urban conditions and remain healthy for any great length of time. This is perhaps even more true of the majority of lichens and for that reason lichens ordinarily are not found in or near cities of even moderate size.

In the vicinity of volcanoes and hot sulphur springs, and also in the vicinity of smelters and other places where large quantities of coal are burned, there are often poisonous gases, mostly sulphurous acid, in the atmosphere which are very injurious to vegetation. The areas thus affected, however, are relatively limited.

Experiments have shown that ordinary air pressures are not at the optimum for vegetative growth of common green plants used in the experiments. It was found in all cases that a decrease in atmospheric pressure, other conditions remaining the same, was accompanied by increased growth. We have no experimental data, however, to indicate whether

the normal atmospheric pressure is at the ecological optimum
for the sum total of the plant's activities.   Probably it is.
A decrease in atmospheric pressure increases the relative
humidity of the air and by so doing has a tendency to check
transpiration.   The decreased pressure at higher altitudes,
however, is ordinarily more than counterbalanced by a
decrease in temperature, and this has the opposite effect on
humidity.   Altogether, therefore, atmospheric pressure is
not of very great importance from an ecological view-point.

87. **Air in Water.**—Air dissolves in water very slowly when
the latter remains still.   Therefore, running water is usually
well aërated, while standing water often is not.   Practically
all seed plants that grow in water possess well-developed air
spaces but this characteristic is much more conspicuous in
plants growing in standing water than in those growing in
running water.

The presence of algæ and other water plants often influences very greatly the amounts of oxygen and carbon dioxide
in water.   In lakes and ponds where algæ are abundant the
water sometimes becomes supersaturated with oxygen as
a result of photosynthesis.   The amount frequently reaches
a saturation of 300 per cent or more.   The same process
prevents the accumulation of large amounts of carbon dioxide.
In this way the algæ become very important in furnishing
a supply of oxygen to the submerged roots of higher plants.
This phenomenon is of especial economic importance in rice
fields where the algæ have been shown to be valuable for
the aëration of the roots of rice plants.

88. **Soil Aëration.**—Roots of different plants vary considerably in their oxygen requirements.   The roots of swamp
plants, for example, require much less oxygen than the
roots of drier land plants.   All roots, however, must carry
on respiration in order to live and so must have some oxygen.
The aëration of the soil, therefore, is very important to the
plants growing in it.

The carbon dioxide that is present in the soil is derived

almost entirely from respiration and decay processes that take place within the soil. Therefore, as would be expected, it regularly increases in amount with the depth of the soil, since at the greater depths it is more difficult for it to escape into the atmosphere. The oxygen of the soil, on the other hand, is obtained from the atmosphere and decreases with an increase in depth of soil. The amounts of carbon dioxide and oxygen in the soil vary greatly at different times of year, with varying conditions of temperature and rainfall, with different types of soil, and with varying kinds and numbers of plants growing in the soil. As would be expected the greatest amount of carbon dioxide is found in the soil in summer and the smallest amount in winter. Ordinarily sand contains the most oxygen and the least carbon dioxide while peat soil is just the opposite in these respects and clay holds an intermediate position. An increased amount of plant growth augments the carbon dioxide and decreases the oxygen supply and similar effects are produced by an increased amount of dead organic matter in the soil.

Since oxygen dissolves very slowly in water a soil that is saturated with water is almost invariably poorly aërated. Plants which ordinarily do not grow in water may be actually drowned if the soil is saturated and there is standing water on the surface for too long a time. This often happens to such crop plants as corn and wheat. These facts are extremely important in irrigation projects. It is almost certain that the usual practice in irrigated regions involves the use of more water than is best for crop production. The plants need both air and water and in general the amount of air increases as the water is decreased. Therefore the most economical practice in irrigation is one that strikes a compromise between these two needs of the plant. The water should be applied in such a way as to interfere as little as possible with the aëration of the soil since otherwise an actual reduction in yield per acre is likely to result.

89. **Atmospheric Humidity.**—The amount of moisture present in the atmosphere, as water vapor, varies greatly from time to time although there is always some present. When the air becomes completely saturated with water condensation begins and some of the water is precipitated as rain or snow. When the atmosphere is saturated with moisture the loss of water from plants by transpiration is negligible and the drier the atmosphere the more rapid is transpiration. The amount of water that the air can hold at any given atmospheric pressure, however, varies directly with the temperature. Therefore, from the ecological point of view, the absolute amount of moisture in the air is not nearly so important as the different between the amount present and the amount necessary to completely saturate it. This difference is called the saturation deficit. It is a measure of the capacity of the atmosphere for taking up water and thus, indirectly, of the rate at which evaporation or transpiration may take place. The amount of moisture present in the air is expressed, not as an absolute amount, but as a percentage of the amount necessary for saturation at a given temperature. This is called the relative humidity. Every change of temperature, of course, changes the relative humidity, without changing the absolute humidity. The saturation deficit, on the other hand, is expressed as weight per cubic foot of air or, more often, as pressure, in inches or centimeters of mercury.

In the measurement of atmospheric humidity use is made of a psychrometer. This instrument consists of two thermometers mounted in such a way that they can readily be whirled to facilitate evaporation. The mercury bulb of one thermometer is covered with cloth which is saturated with water. The evaporation of the water cools the thermometer and the difference between the readings of the two thermometers is called the depression of the wet bulb. Tables have been worked out for nearly all possible combinations of air temperatures and wet bulb depressions showing relative humidities and dew points, the dew point being the temperature at which condensation would take place with the existing water vapor, that is, the temperature at which the air would become saturated without any increase in the absolute humidity. The tables most used in American are the "Psychrometric Tables" of the United States Weather Bureau, contained in its Bulletin 235. From these tables the relative humidity may be obtained directly and the saturation deficit is obtained by taking the difference between the saturation pressure at the current dry bulb temperature and the saturation pressure at the current dew point. Such data, when extended over a long period of time, are very useful in determining whether the environment is suited to plants that are well protected from excessive transpiration or to those that are relatively unprotected.

90. **Wind.**—Wind is moving air and is more important from an ecological view point than is still air. Its effect on plants is both physical and physiological. The breaking-over and uprooting of plants and the breaking of branches are familiar examples of the physical effect of wind. Wind is also important as an agent of pollination and of dispersal. It has already been discussed as an agent of pollination in Chapter VI and its action in the dispersal of seeds and fruits will be taken up later in connection with the subject of plant succession.

The physiological effect of wind consists almost entirely in increasing transpiration, and in this capacity it is very important. As a rule, the velocity of the wind increases with the height above the ground. Therefore, the tallest plants, such as trees, suffer most from the drying effects of the winds, while low plants, such as many grasses, get along very well in windy regions. Furthermore, the height to which many plants can grow is limited by their ability to transport water upward fast enough to counteract the loss through transpiration. For this reason, in the most windy places, such as exposed mountain ridges and flat windy sea-coasts, tall plants are entirely absent.

Because of this drying effect of the wind the trees are

smaller on the windward side of an exposed grove than on
the opposite side. A single tree growing in the open is
almost invariably one-sided; that is, a larger part of its

Fig. 62.—"Elfin timber." Engleman spruce at timber line in the Arapaho
National forest, Colorado.

Fig. 63.—Dwarf vegetation at the top of Specimen Mountain, Colorado,
Silene acaulis in the center.

crown is on the side opposite that from which the prevailing winds blow. So true is this that one can determine the direction of the prevailing winds of a region by examining the trees.

At timber line on mountains the same species of woody plants, which a few hundred feet further down are upright forest trees, grow as gnarled and sprawling, much-branched shrubs, known as elfin-timber (Fig. 62). The short growing season, the low temperature of the soil, and the drying effect of the winds, make conditions here so difficult for growth that a tree may be several hundred years old yet only a few inches in diameter of trunk and a foot or so in height. Above timber line on the higher mountains a similar effect is seen in the herbaceous vegetation, all of the plants being very dwarf (Fig. 63).

91. Cold-air Drainage.—Cold air is heavier than warm air. It therefore has a tendency to settle down into low places and displace the warmer air that is there. This takes place to a certain extent each night as the air is cooling after sundown. For this reason there are usually frosts later in spring and earlier in autumn in the lowlands than on the uplands. Peaches, strawberries, and other crop plants that are subject to late frosts in spring, are more profitable on highlands than in valleys, because they more often escape the effects of late frosts.

REFERENCES.

Bergman, H. F.: The Effect of Cloudiness on the Oxygen Content of Water and its Significance in Cranberry Culture, Am. Jour. Bot., 1921, **8**, 50–58.

Bergman, H. F.: The Relation of Aëration to the Growth and Activity of Roots and Its Influence on the Ecesis of Plants in Swamps, Ann. Bot., 1920, **34**, 13–33.

Cannon, W. A.: Physiological Features of Roots with Special Reference to the Relation of Roots to the Aëration of the Soils, Carnegie Inst. Washington Publ., 1925, **368**, 169.

Clements, Frederic E.: Aëration and Air-content, the Role of Oxygen in Root Activity, Carnegie Inst. Washington Publ., 1921, **315**, 183.

Hubert, E. E.: Fungi as Contributory Causes of Windfall in the Northwest, Jour. Forestry, 1918, **16**, 696–714.

Shreve, Forrest: Cold-air Drainage, Plant World, 1912, **15**, 110–115.

CHAPTER XIII.

SOIL.

SOIL is the weathered superficial layer of the earth's surface mingled to a greater or less extent with the remains of plants and animals. It is used by the great majority of plants as the chief source of inorganic food materials and water and for mechanical support. There are some plants, principally the floating water plants, that make no use at all of soil, and most parasites and epiphytes make no direct use of soil, though, in most cases the plants on which they live must have it. Soils differ very greatly in physical and chemical properties and in various other respects and these differences have very important influences upon plant life.

92. **Soil Formation.**—All soils are formed primarily from rocks. Plants play an important part in the formation of soils. This is done in part directly by the disintegration of rocks by the plants growing on them. The only plants that can live on strictly unweathered rocks are certain kinds of lichens. These, however, have a disintegrating effect on the rock surface so that gradually a thin layer of soil is formed and this enables mosses and some other plants to get a start. The disintegration of the rock now goes on more rapidly as the numbers of plants increase. The underlying rocks are split apart and broken into pieces by the roots of plants growing in cracks and crevices (Fig. 64). Thus the building of a soil goes on apace. At the same time whole plants or the deciduous parts of plants are each year dying and adding the material of their bodies to the soil. A deep, black, humus soil, such as is often found in a forest, represents the remains of thousands of generations of plants.

Another way in which plants add to the soil of a given area is by the accumulation of materials that are being carried by

wind or water. This is more readily seen in some places
than in others. For example, the flattened leaves of the
stag-horn fern accumulate considerable quantities of soil,
and a zone of plants such as water lilies along the edge of a
glacial lake will often accumulate masses of materials of all
sorts. But this sort of accumulation is going on more or less
wherever plants are growing.

FIG. 64.—Soil formation on sandstone rock. Plants growing in the crevices.

Rock masses are often built up through the activities of
plants. This is done largely by algæ which absorb soluble
materials from the water and secrete them in an insoluble
form. Marl is built up in this way by Chara while strata
of silica are built up by diatoms. A few algæ store up lime in
a comparable way. In fact limestone is usually built up by
some such means and the material of coral reefs, formerly
thought to be built up entirely by corals, is now known to
12

be due in part, at least, to the activities of algæ. The travertine deposits around hot springs are also built up largely by algæ.

93. **Soil Structure and Classification.**—A soil ordinarily consists of a mixture of rock particles, water containing dissolved substances, air, dead organic matter and living plants and animals. The relative amounts of these various components vary greatly in different soils. Leaving out of consideration for the present the living organisms, about 40 per cent, by volume, of a rich garden soil is rock particles; 25 per cent is water, 25 per cent air and 10 per cent organic matter.

Soils may be classified in various ways. It will serve our purpose to classify them simply as sand, clay, and humus, though most soils consist of mixtures of two or all of these types. Perhaps the most important difference between the three general types of soil is in the size of the soil particles. Humus has the smallest soil particles and sand the largest, while clay is intermediate in this respect. Humus also differs from the other two types in being composed of organic matter.

94. **Soil Water.**—The water-holding capacity of a soil is one of the most important of all soil factors and is dependent upon the size of the soil particles. The chief, and usually the only, source of soil water is rain. A considerable percentage of the rainfall in any year flows off from the surface of the soil and is of no use to plants. This part is called the run-off and it may do a great amount of damage by washing away portions of the soil. The remainder of the rain enters the soil and the soil becomes wet. If it continues to rain after the soil is thoroughly wet the water percolates downward under the influence of gravity until it reaches the level of standing water where all the soil spaces are completely filled. This level is called the water table and its depth varies greatly from place to place and from season to season. The water that remains in the soil above the water table is

capillary water. It remains because the attraction of the soil particles for it is great enough to overcome the pull of gravity. This water, therefore, is a measure of the water-holding capacity of the soil and since the total amount of surface of soil particles increases as their size decreases we would expect a fine-grain soil to be capable of holding more water than a coarse-grain soil. Experiments have shown that an average sand soil will hold 20 to 25 per cent of its volume of water, while clay will hold 32 to 40 per cent, and humus 65 to 70 per cent. Not all of this water is available to plants, however. The total water in a soil is known as holard, while the part that is available to plants is called chresard, and that which is not available is echard. The echard, then, is the water that clings so closely to the soil particles that plants cannot get it. The echard as well as the holard, varies in different soils. The echard in sand is only about 2 to 2.5 per cent of the volume of the soil, while that in clay is 6.5 to 7 per cent, and that in humus 8 to 8.5 per cent. It is because of this difference in the echard that plants often seem to get along pretty well in sand which is so dry that it feels dry to the hand, a phenomenon that is much less true of clay or humus.

The echard, it must be said, is not determined entirely by the type of soil since some plants can absorb more water from a given soil than can others. It is usually necessary in ecological work, therefore, to determine the echard for the particular species being studied. There are several ways of doing this, the most direct method being to grow a plant in the soil until it wilts beyond recovery and to determine the amount of moisture that is then present in the soil. This amount of moisture is taken as the wilting coefficient for the species of plant, and the type of soil, used.

After rain has ceased falling, evaporation may take place from the surface of the soil. This reverses the direction of water movement in the soil, since as the surface layers dry out water comes up from below by the process of capillarity.

It is well known that when a small glass tube is lowered into a jar of water the water rises in the tube some distance above the level in the jar. This is due to capillarity. If a larger tube is used the water does not rise so far because the weight of the column of water partly overcomes the capillary attraction between the glass and the water. Likewise, the distance to which water will ascend in a soil depends on the size of the soil particles since this governs the size of the capillary spaces between particles. Water may be raised by capillarity to distances varying from about a foot to as much as 5 feet in different soils.

95. **Chemical Composition of Soil.**—Ten chemical elements are necessary as food materials. These are carbon, hydrogen, oxygen, nitrogen, sulphur, phosphorus, potassium, calcium, magnesium and iron. The first three of these are obtained from carbon dioxide and water. The other seven are absorbed from the soil in the form of soluble salts.

The rocks from which sand and clay are formed usually consist largely of silica and alumina and a few other oxides that are entirely unavailable as food materials. Mixed with these oxides, however, are small quantities of compounds containing the plant nutrients. Many rocks lack certain nutrients entirely, but since most soils are of rather complex origin there are usually some of all the essential elements present. However, they are present in varying amounts and they may be lost by being leached out by percolating water or by the removal of crop plants that have grown on the soil in question. It is often necessary, therefore, to replace certain of the essential elements in order to maintain the fertility of the soil.

Iron is used by plants only in very minute quantities and is usually present in the soil in rather large quantities. It is very seldom necessary, therefore, to add iron to agricultural soil. Sulphur is used in rather large amounts and is ordinarily present in the soil in relatively small amounts. Sulphur, however, is washed into the soil by rain. Experiments have shown that in Illinois an average of 40 pounds of sulphur per acre is added to the soil annually by this means and this appears to be enough to maintain the supply indefinitely. It is seldom necessary to add magnesium to a soil. Potassium is abundant in most soils but in the case of peaty soils it is often necessary to add potassium, usually in the form of the sulphate. Calcium, when needed, may be profitably added, usually, in the form of pulverized limestone, and phosphorus in the form of powdered rock phosphate. Limestone not only adds calcium to the soil but corrects the acidity of soils that have become "sour." The most practical means of keeping up the nitrogen supply in the soil is to grow legume crops periodically so that the nitrogen-fixing bacteria may build up nitrates from atmospheric nitrogen. Of course, when sufficient manure is available for addition to a soil often nothing else is needed since manure ordinarily contains all of the necessary mineral nutrients.

Although there is, as we have indicated, an abundance of inorganic salts in most soils, the actual concentration of salts in solution in the soil water is not high. There are very few plants that can use a 5 per cent salt solution and many plants are killed by concentrations much less than this. There are some plants, however, that can endure considerable amounts of salt in the soil. Thus we find that saline regions have very characteristic floras, and salt waters also have floras that are characteristically different from those of fresh waters. Many marine algæ cannot live at all in fresh water. Some fungi, likewise are able to grow in very high concentrations. A mold, for example, has been observed growing in a can of karo syrup.

Many elements in addition to those that have been shown to be essential are absorbed to a certain extent by plants and probably each one has some physiological effect upon the plant. Some elements which are almost universally poisonous to plants, such as copper and zinc, are found in the ash of certain plants, and, in fact, growth seems to be stimulated in some plants by the presence of small quantities of these poisonous elements in the soil.

96. Soil Acidity and Alkalinity.—Although a considerable amount of work has been done on the relation of plants to the specific acidity or alkalinity of the soil, the subject is still very imperfectly understood. The important factor seems to be the hydrogen-ion concentration of the soil solution, rather than the actual amount of acid present, and it is usually determined by means of colorimetric indicators.

FIG. 65.—*Kalmia latifolia.* A plant of acid soils. (Photograph by A. G. Eldredge.)

Some plants, such as *Pellæa atropurpurea,* the cliff-brake fern, are so characteristic of limestone soils that it is often possible to tell whether lime is present in the soil merely by observing the vegetation. Sweet clover, *Melilotus alba,* and black locust, *Robinia pseudo-acacea,* are other plants that flourish where there is an abundance of lime though they are not strictly limited to such situations. On the other hand such plants as blueberries (*Vaccinium*), mountain laurel (*Kalmia*) (Fig. 65) and azaleas (*Rhododendron*), grow only in acid soils. It has been found that these plants can be grown in ordinary soils if the soil is kept acid by some means, as by the addition of aluminum sulphate or of tannic acid. These acid-requiring plants, however, are all endotrophic mycorhizal plants and it seems likely that it is the mycorhizal fungi rather than the higher plants that require acid conditions. This is made to appear all the more probable by the fact that large numbers of non-mycorhizal plants, including many ferns, spring flowers, and others, have been found growing in soils ranging from definite alkalinity to high acidity.

97. **Unstable Soils.**—In order that soil may be used by plants it must remain reasonably quiet. The most notable examples of unstable soils are found in sand dune areas along sea coasts and in other regions of drifting sand hills. Very few plants can grow on shifting sand dunes. In the case of such dunes the sand is constantly being blown up from behind and dumped in front so that the dune gradually moves along in the direction toward which the wind is blowing. Plants that may be growing on the sand near the rear of the dune, therefore, are likely to be torn out by the roots or at least to have their roots uncovered and exposed to the drying air. On the other hand, plants growing in the path of the dune may be buried by the sand. A large dune may even overwhelm a forest and, passing on, leave it a veritable cemetery of dead trees.

There are, however, certain grasses and a few other plants, known as "sand binders," which are capable of growing on shifting sand and often help to stop its motion (Fig. 66). Their stems elongate as the sand piles up around them so that their tops are kept above the surface and at the same time adventitious roots are developed on the buried portions so that the distance from the top of the plant to its nearest roots is never excessive. Some trees, as for example the cottonwood, *Populus deltoides,* have this same ability, to a considerable extent. A cottonwood tree may become two or more times its normal height as the sand piles up around it but by putting out adventitious roots into the sand the distance from the top of the tree to the source of water supply is kept normal.

Fig. 66.—*Ammophila arenaria* (beach grass) and *Hudsonia tomentosa,* two sand-binding plants. (Photograph by A. G. Eldredge.)

Another sort of instability of soil is that caused by water erosion. This takes place along streams and on unprotected hillsides and often is very destructive to vegetation. When a hillside is covered with forest practically no erosion is possible, but when such a forest is removed gulleying often sets in. Large areas have in some places been made useless for agricultural purposes by thoughtlessly removing the forest from an adjacent hillside. In such a case erosion starts on the hillside and rapidly cuts back into the level upland. The "bad lands" of North and South Dakota and Nebraska, which have been produced through erosion, are in some portions almost destitute of plant life (Fig. 67).

98. **Soil Covers.**—The presence, or absence, of a soil cover is a factor of considerable importance. Soil covers may be living or non-living. The more important effects of a non-living cover are protection against loss of water and against rapid changes of temperature. If the soil repeatedly freezes and thaws during the winter many plants are "heaved" upward, their roots are more or less broken, and they may

FIG. 67.—"Bad Lands," Sioux Co., Nebraska. Produced by water erosion. (Photograph by Raymond J. Pool.)

suffer death from loss of water through exposure to the air. An efficient soil cover largely prevents this. A covering of snow is perhaps the most effective of all soil covers in protecting low plants from wind and from rapid temperature changes. The effect of a snow cover is well seen in some Arctic regions where many woody plants are entirely unable to endure the cold dry winds of winter if unprotected. Such plants grow upward each summer as far as is possible in the limited time but each winter they are killed back to the level

of the snow so that they are kept constantly in the condition
of shrubs, their height being limited by the depth of the snow.
It is well known to farmers that fall-sown wheat stands the
winter better if it is protected by a covering of snow.

A covering of leaves and withered grass or other plant
remains serves the same function as a covering of snow though
not as efficiently. A living cover serves to a certain extent
in the same way as a non-living one but is more important
in what it takes from and what it adds to the soil. It also,
of course, serves to stabilize the soil and prevent it from being
blown or washed away. If the living cover consists of mosses
it may be as efficient as a non-living cover in protecting
against loss of water from the soil since the moss plants take
very little moisture from the soil themselves and they form
a very compact cover.

99. **Soil Floras and Faunas.**—The plants and animals that
spend all or a part of their lives entirely within the soil
make up a group of soil factors of which we are in need of
much more study. They are very important to the higher
plants though just how important cannot yet be said, at
least in many cases. Every soil that contains any humus
material has some fungi. The role played by these fungi is
by no means well known. Some of them bring about decay,
some have mycorhizal relations with seed plants, and there
are probably other interrelations that we do not yet understand. The bacteria are probably of even greater importance
than the fungi. There are myriads of bacteria present in all
soils: nitrogen-fixing bacteria, nitrifying and denitrifying
bacteria, bacteria of fermentation, of decay, etc. As many
as a million bacteria have been found in a single gram of soil.
There are also many algæ, especially blue-green algæ, that
are found in soils and that probably are of importance to the
higher plants.

Earthworms play a very important role in soil fertility
partly through the fact that their tunnels aid in the aëration
of the soil and more largely through the fact that they mix

the soil by bringing the subsoil to the surface. It has been estimated that in some localities earthworms bring up as much as 18 tons of subsoil per acre annually and it is probable that every particle of soil to a considerable depth is worked over by earthworms within a few years. Burrowing rodents serve in about the same way and where they are very numerous they may be as important as earthworms. Moles aid to a certain extent in mixing and aërating the soil and, on the other hand, they destroy many plants by burrowing through their root systems.

Ants are also important soil mixers in some localities, it having been estimated that they may bring as much as $\frac{1}{5}$ inch of new soil to the surface each year. There are many other kinds of insects found in the soil, but their activities are not well known. Some counts of the numbers of animals in the surface layer of soil have shown 2,250,000 per acre in a forest and 13,500,000 in a pasture. In both cases a very large percentage of the animals were insects.

100. Edaphic Factors and the Distribution of Plants.— Ecological factors which are entirely local in their effects are called edaphic factors in contrast with climatic factors which are usually much less limited in their areas of activity. All soil factors are local in their effects and for this reason the term edaphic, as applied to factors, has come to refer almost exclusively to soil factors.

Plant distribution within limited areas is determined almost entirely by edaphic factors. This fact is well expressed by what we may call Schimper's Second Law which states that "The local distribution of plants and of plant communities is determined chiefly by the nature of the soil, either directly, or in its relation to other factors."

REFERENCES.

Alway, F. J., McDole, G. R. and Trumbull, R. S.: Relation of Minimum Moisture Content of Subsoil of Prairies to Hygroscopic Coefficient, Bot. Gaz., 1919, **67**, 185–207.

Atkins, W. R. G.:   Some Factors Affecting the Hydrogen-ion Concentration of the Soil and its Relation to Plant Distribution, Notes Bot. School Trinity Coll. (Dublin), 1922, **3**, 133–177.

Burgess, Paul S. and Pember, F. R.:   "Active" Aluminum as a Factor Detrimental to Crop Production in Many Acid Soils, Rhode Island Agr. Exp. Sta. Bull., 1923, **194**, 1–40, fig. 1–5.

Clark, G. R.:   Soil Acidity and its Relation to the Production of Nitrate and Ammonia in Woodland Soils, Oxford Forest, Mem., 1924, **2**, 1–27, 3 fig.

Fisher, F. A.:   Soil Relation, Sci. Prog., 1925, **16**, 408–425.

Johnson, James and Hartman, R. E.:   Influence of Soil Environment on the Root-rot of Tobacco, Jour. Agr. Res., 1919, **17**, 41–86.

Kurz, Herman: Hydrogen-ion Concentration in Relation to Ecological Factors, Bot. Gaz., 1923, **76**, 1–29, fig. 1–4.

Marbut, C. F.:   Soils of the Great Plains (U. S. A.), Ann. Assn. Am. Geog., 1923, **13**, 41–66, 2 pl. 2 fig.

Moore, Barrington: Influence of Certain Soil Factors on the Growth of Tree Seedlings and Wheat, Ecology, 1922, **3**, 65–83, 6 fig.

Moore, G. T. and Karrer, J. K.:   A Subterranean Algal Flora, Ann. Missouri Bot. Gard., 1919, **6**, 281–307.

Olsen, Carsten: Studies on the Hydrogen-ion Concentration of the Soil and its Significance to the Vegetation, Especially to the Natural Distribution of Plants, Compt. Rend. Trans. Lab. Carlsberg (Copenhagen), 1923, **151**, 1–166, 27, fig.

Russell, Edward J.:   Soil Conditions and Plant Growth, 4th ed. XII p. 406, 32 fig., Longmans, Green and Co., London, 1921.

Salisbury, E. J.:   Stratification and Hydrogen-ion Concentration of the Soil in Relation to Leaching and Plant Succession with Special Reference to Woodlands, Jour. Ecol., 1922, **9**, 220–240.

Shantz, H. L.:   Drought Resistance and Soil Moisture, Ecology, 1927, **8**, 145–157.

Wherry, Edgar T.:   Observations on the Soil Acidity of Ericaceæ and Associated Plants in the Middle Atlantic States, Proc. Acad. Nat. Sci., Philadelphia, 1920, **72**, 84–111.

Wherry, Edgar T.:   Soil Acidity and a Field Method for its Measurement, Ecology, 1920, **1**, 160–173.

Wherry, Edgar T.:   The Soil Reactions of the Ferns of Woods and Swamps, Am. Fern Jour., 1921, **11**, 5–6.

CHAPTER XIV.

WATER.

WATER is the most important single factor in the environment of plants. The amount needed by different kinds of plants varies greatly but some is necessary for every living organism. It is of vital importance to the plant in several ways. For example, it is a necessary constituent of all protoplasm as well as of cell sap. It is a food material necessary in carbohydrate synthesis. All inorganic food materials are absorbed and transported in a water solution. The resistance of a plant to heat or cold is largely determined by the amount of water present. Finally, water has more influence on the external and internal structure of plants than any other factor.

Several phases of the water factor have been discussed in preceding chapters. There are a number of other facts about the water relation, however, that it is necessary for us to understand and these will be taken up in the present chapter.

101. **The Classification of Plants on the Basis of Water Relation.**—Plants are found growing in all sorts of conditions with respect to water supply. Some live on rocks where the amount of water available is extremely limited, others are immersed in water where the supply is inexhaustible, while still others are found in all degrees of gradation between these extremes. Those plants that can get along with small amounts of water are called xerophytes. Those that can endure large amounts of water are called hydrophytes. Those that get along best with medium amounts of water are called mesophytes. The majority of plants are readily classified into one of these three groups. There are, however, large numbers that are intermediate between two groups and

rather difficult to classify satisfactorily. For this reason we frequently find it convenient to use such terms as xero-mesophyte, to indicate a plant that is somewhat more xeric (characterized by scanty moisture supply) than a typical mesophyte, meso-zerophyte, for one that is somewhat less xeric than a typical xerophyte; hydro-mesophyte, for one that is somewhat more hydric (characterized by abundant moisture supply) than a typical mesophyte, etc. It is also customary to use such combinations as shade-mesophyte, sun-hydrophyte, alpine-xerophyte, etc., in order to more accurately define the type of plant under discussion.

There are some plants that change from one group to another at different seasons. Familiar examples of this phenomenon are the deciduous trees of the temperate zones. The majority of these trees, such, for example, as *Acer saccharum*, the sugar maple, are typical mesophytes in summer when they have leaves but are xerophytes in winter when they are leafless. Such plants are called tropophytes.

Some of the characteristic differences between xerophytes, mesophytes, and hydrophytes have been brought out in the discussion of the ecology of stems and leaves and others will be taken up in a later chapter. It is necessary to point out here, however, that this classification of plants does not depend so much upon the actual amount of water present in the immediate environment as upon the relation between absorption and transpiration. In some cases the cause of xerism is an actual inadequate water supply, as in deserts, but in other cases it may be due to physiological dryness; that is, to difficulty of absorption, as in saline regions or in peat bogs; or it may be due more largely to high transpiration as in some alpine regions. The chief causes of hydrism, on the other hand, are a saturated atmosphere or an abundance of soil water, or both.

102. **Transpiration.**—When a land plant is in an active condition there is a more or less constant stream of water passing through it. The water is absorbed into the roots,

transported upward through the xylem, and transpired from the surfaces of the leaves. The plant actually uses a considerable amount of water but it absorbs and transpires a great deal more than it needs for its ordinary metabolic processes. The amount passing through the plant varies greatly at different times and sometimes is surprisingly large. It has been estimated for example that a beech tree, one hundred years old, transpires about 60 barrels of water during a season, and that a field of corn transpires during its entire season of growth as much water as would amount to 5 inches of rain on the field. Actual measurements during a period of ten days of dry weather have shown that corn transpired from 6 to 9 times its own dry weight daily while alfalfa transpired from 36 to 56 times its own dry weight. On the basis of 1 ton of dry matter per acre this would amount to a daily loss of 0.05 to 0.08 of an acre inch of water daily from the cornfield and of 0.32 to 0.49 of an acre inch from the alfalfa field.

Of course all plants do not transpire so rapidly as those we have cited. It has been estimated that sun mesophytes, such as alfalfa, often transpire at least 175,000 times as rapidly, per unit area, as some of the desert shrubs, such as *Fouquieria splendens*, the ocotilla, when they are leafless. It has been shown in the case of several kinds of emersed water plants that water is lost more rapidly from a given area occupied by plants than from an equal area of free water surface. In the case of water lilies, however, the reverse was true.

The process of transpiration is thought to be of very great importance to the plant because of its cooling effect. Yet the greatest danger to which many plants are subjected is that of too great a loss of water. The various ways in which plants are protected from this danger are discussed in Chapter IV.

103. **The Mechanical Effects of Water.**—Water sometimes has destructive effects upon plants. Heavy storms of rain

or hail may beat down and destroy seedlings or they may tear or knock off leaves, flowers, or fruits. Snow, which is a form of water, may break down plants or plant parts by its weight. In some places in mountainous regions snow collects near the mountain top and when thawing starts in spring the snow comes down the mountain in a gigantic snow-slide, breaking down the woody plants in its path. When this is repeated in the same path year after year the development of a forest is completely prevented. Such snow-slide paths are often several hundred feet wide. Snow, on the other hand, may be of very great value to plants by serving as a protective covering during the winter. A sleet storm is very destructive in breaking down woody plants. There is also danger of trees being smothered when sleet remains on them for a long time, though probably this does not happen often.

Water is of considerable importance as an agent of pollination and in the dissemination of seeds and fruits, but these matters are discussed elsewhere.

104. **Rainfall.**—Whenever air is cooled to such an extent that it cannot hold in a vaporous state as much water as it contains, the water falls as rain, hail, or snow, or is deposited as dew. These forms of precipitation are the chief source of water for most plants. Some plants, such as numerous epiphytes and many lichens and mosses, especially those growing upon rocks, absorb all of their water directly from atmospheric precipitations. Ordinary land plants, on the other hand, get most of their water indirectly from rainfall after it has penetrated into the soil.

The annual amount of rainfall varies greatly in different places and from season to season. The locations of large bodies of water and of mountain ranges and the direction of the prevailing winds are important factors in determining the amount of annual rainfall in any region. In the continental United States the regions of greatest rainfall are found in the northwest and in the extreme southeast. Leaving out of consideration the effects of local topographic features the amount of rainfall gradually decreases from Florida toward the north and west, and from Washington and Oregon toward the south and east. The region of

FIG. 68.—Forest vegetation, Norway and jack pines, Minnesota. (Photograph by A. G. Gaskill. Courtesy of H. L. Shantz and the U. S. Department of Agriculture.)

least rainfall, on the other hand, is found in the southwestern part of the United States and, in general, it increases in amount from New Mexico and Arizona toward the north and

13

east. In much the greater part of the United States the larger part of the rain falls in summer. In some regions of the southwest, however, especially in southern California, the larger part, in some cases more than 80 per cent, falls in winter. The seasonal distribution of rain not only has a marked effect upon the distribution of the types of vegetation, as will be brought out in the following paragraph, but is also one of the chief causes of certain periodic phenomena in plants

FIG. 69.—Grassland vegetation, Oregon. (Photograph by H. L. Shantz. Courtesy of H. L. Shantz and the U. S. Department of Agriculture.)

such as rest periods. An adequate supply of moisture is absolutely necessary for active growth and, therefore, if at any time it becomes inadequate it may bring about a resting period, or it may cause death.

105. **Water as a Factor in the Distribution of Plants.**—If we disregard small local areas and consider only large regions, a birds-eye view of the land surface of the earth shows three general types of vegetation; namely, forest (Fig. 68), grass-

land (Fig. 69) and desert (Fig. 70). These rather distinct types are determined largely by the amount of rainfall, the seasonal distribution of the rainfall, and the frequency of rainy days or of effective rains. By effective rains we mean rains that actually supply water to the plants. Light showers are often entirely ineffective because the water evaporates before it has penetrated the soil far enough to be available to the roots. On the other hand, during a torrential rain there may be such a great run-off that only a small fraction of the water that falls becomes available to

FIG. 70.—Desert vegetation with *Ferocactus acanthodes* most prominent. Colorado desert, California. (Photograph by W. S. Cooper.)

the plants. If, therefore, a large percentage of the rain falls in light showers or torrential storms it may be considerably less effective than a much smaller total precipitation which falls in such a way as to be largely absorbed by the soil. The frequency of effective rains and the seasonal distribution of the rainfall are, therefore, usually more important than the amount of the annual precipitation.

In general, forests occur in regions where there is adequate rainfall during all seasons of the year. There must also be a warm vegetative season and, if there is a winter the atmosphere must be reasonably moist in order that transpiration may be reduced, since the trees are always exposed to transpiration and they cannot absorb water from a frozen soil. In regions of high winter rainfall and low summer rainfall, such as occurs in parts of southern California, the sclero-

Fig. 71.—*Arctostaphylos viscida*, a broad-leaf sclerophyll. Grass valley, California. (Photograph by W. S. Cooper.)

phyllous type of forest, composed of low trees or shrubs with broad, sclerophyllous, evergreen leaves, is found (Fig. 71).

Grasslands occur chiefly in regions of high summer rainfall and low winter rainfall, while deserts occur where there is low rainfall both winter and summer. If we represent the summer season by the letter S and the winter by W, using a large letter for a high rainfall and a small letter for a low rainfall in each case, the amounts of rainfall needed by the different types of vegetation may be represented symbolically as follows:

SW-ordinary forest.   Sw-grassland.

sW-sclerophyllous forest.   sw-desert.

It may be seen by the following diagram that there may be transition from one to another of the types in all cases except between sclerophyllous forests and grasslands.

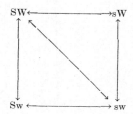

The influence of water on the distribution of the vegetation types is well brought out by what we may call Schimper's Third Law. This states that the type of vegetation in the tropical and temperate zones is determined by the amount and seasonal distribution of the rainfall and by the humidity of the air.

REFERENCES.

Batchelor, L. D. and Reed, H. S.:   The Seasonal Variation of the Soil Moisture in a Walnut Grove in Relation to the Hygroscopic Coefficient, California Agric. Exp. Sta. Tech. Paper, 1923, **10**, 31, 2 fig.

Freeman, George F.:   Studies in Evaporation and Transpiration, Bot. Gaz., 1920, **70**, 190–210, 5 fig.

Fritch, F. V. and Haines, F. M.:   The Moisture Relations of Terrestrial Algæ.   II. The Changes During Exposure to Drought and Treatment with Hypertonic Solutions, Ann. Bot., 1923, **37**, 683–728, 8 fig.

Harris, F. S.:   The Duty of Water in Cache Valley, Utah, Utah Agric. Exp. Sta. Bull., 1919, **168**, 23 p. 70 fig.

Hume, A. N., Loomis, H. and Hutton, J. G.:   Water as a Limiting Factor in the Growth of Sweet Clover (Melilotus alba), South Dakota Agric. Exp. Sta. Bull., 1920, **191**, 44 p. 2 pl., 3 fig.

Jones, J. S., Colver, C. W. and Fishburn, H. P.:   The Protein Content of Wheat Grown with Irrigation, Jour. Agric. Sci., 1920, **10**, 290–232, fig. 1–11.

Kiesselbach, T. A.:   Transpiration as a Factor in Crop Production, Nebraska Agric. Exp. Station Res. Bull., 1916, **6**, 214.

Pool, Raymond J.:   Xerophytism and Comparative Leaf Anatomy in Relation to Transpiring Power, Bot. Gaz., 1920, **70**, 190–210, 5 fig.

Trelease, Sam. F.:   Incipient Drying and Wilting as Indicated by Movements of Coconut Pinnæ, Am. Jour. Bot., 1922, **9**, 253–265, 1 fig.

Tulaikov, N. M.:   The Utilization of Water by Plants Under Field and Greenhouse Conditions, Soil Sci., 1926, **25**, 75–91.

Shreve, Edith B.:   Seasonal Changes in the Water Relations of Desert Plants, Ecology, 1923, **4**, 266–292, figs. 1–11.

CHAPTER XV.

GROWTH HABITS OF PLANTS.

VARIOUS attempts have been made from time to time to classify plants into life-form groups and to interpret these groups in terms of the environment. These classifications have been founded, for the most part, on the role played by a particular species in vegetation and its life history under the conditions prevailing in its habitat, with special reference to duration, propagation and protection during unfavorable seasons. These classifications have not proven so useful as their authors hoped, largely, perhaps, because we still are unable to interpret ecologically many of the growth-forms that we find, but such classifications are of considerable value in certain types of ecological work.

The simplest classification of this sort is the one we have already given; namely, the classification into xerophytes, mesophytes, and hydrophytes, although it is based only on a single relation, that of water supply. In this chapter we shall first discuss some of the characteristics of these three general types of plants and then consider briefly two other classifications that have been used.

106. **Plants of Hydric Habitats.**—The habitat of a plant consists of the sum total of the environmental conditions under which it lives. Hydric habitats are those occupied by hydric plants (Fig. 72). They may differ from one another in various ways but all agree in containing an abundance of available water. In response to a degree of uniformity of environment plant forms have developed with certain characteristics that may be taken as more or less distinctive of plants of hydric habitats.

(199)

A pond or small lake may be taken as typical of extreme hydric habitats. Characteristic plants of such a habitat are many algæ, duckweeds, pond lilies, etc. Root systems are much reduced both in length and in amount of branching. Root hairs are absent in the water though they may be present where the roots extend into the mud below. Leaves often equal or surpass roots as absorbing organs. Those

Fig. 72.—A marsh in California. The vegetation is almost exclusively *Scirpus validus* (great bulrush), a typical hydrophyte. (Photograph by H. L. Shantz. Courtesy of H. L. Shantz and the U. S. Department of Agriculture.)

of submerged plants are thin and often finely dissected. Air spaces often exceed the tissue in actual volume. Stomata are absent in submerged leaves and are present only on the upper surfaces of floating leaves. Such stomata as are present have but slightly cutinized walls and are almost always open. Protective features are few or wanting. Cutin and cork rarely are developed below the surface of the water, hairs are scarce, and the cell sap has a low osmotic pressure. Conducting and mechanical tissues are also greatly reduced.

The absence of protective features is, of course, not disadvantageous to the plants because absorption is easy and below the surface of the water transpiration is practically absent. The submerged portions of seed plants are usually covered with slime which harbors communities of bacteria and other low organisms. The aërial surfaces of floating organs, on the other hand, are usually coated with wax and so are not easily wet. Vegetative reproduction is highly developed in hydric habitats, while flowers and seeds are less abundant than in most habitats.

Fɪɢ. 73.—Skunk cabbage (*Symplocarpus fœtidus*). Plants of swampy places.

A swamp (Figs. 73 and 74) is a hydric habitat which differs from a pond or lake in that the water table is just about at the surface of the soil, though it may be a little above during wet seasons or a little below during dry seasons. Some characteristic swamp plants are the cat-tails (*Typha*), the reed (*Phragmites*), the bulrush (*Scirpus*), etc. The structural features of swamp plants are in part like those of pond plants, especially in the reduced root systems and prominent air chambers, but, in general, they are less extremely hydric and have a tendency to approach a resemblance to mesophytes. Roots of swamp plants are frequently horizontal, or even ascending, rather than descending. Rhizomes are greatly developed and there is an abundant development of vertical chlorophyll-bearing organs, whether stems or leaves.

107. **Plants of Xeric Habitats.**—There are two general types of xeric habitats, those in which there is an actual dearth of water and those which contain an abundance of

Fig. 74.—A cat-tail swamp. The most abundant plant is *Typha latifolia*, a hydrophyte.

water but are physiologically dry. The latter will be discussed in Paragraph 108.

The most typical of the true xeric habitats are found in desert regions where such plants as sage brush and the various kinds of cacti are characteristic (Fig. 75). The roots frequently are strongly developed, possessing either considerable length or great size, though this is generally not true of cacti. Roots that have great size serve to accumulate large amounts of water. Root hairs are abundant, often extending far back from the root tip, and in some cases having thick, rigid cell walls. Palisade tissue is strongly developed and the chlorenchyma in both leaves and stems is often deep-seated so that these organs have a pale green color.

Protective features are remarkably well developed and of course are needed because of the great exposure of xerophytes to transpiration. The transpiring surface is usually relatively reduced, the leaves, if present, being small and thick. Many species are leafless, their cylindrical stems exposing a relatively small surface to transpiration while their vertical orientation affords some protection from the intense rays

Fig. 75.—*Yucca arborescens.* A desert xerophyte. (Photograph by W. S. Cooper.)

of sunlight during the middle of the day. In many cases there is a temporary reduction of transpiring surface, as in the leaves of grasses which roll up and those of legumes which fold during the hottest and dryest parts of the day. Temporary reduction is exhibited also by those deciduous plants which shed their leaves at the beginning of each period of dry or cold weather. Annuals, which live through the critical season only as seeds, represent the extreme of temporary reduction of transpiration surface. Dwarfness of habit is a prominent xeric feature and the resulting compactness in arrangement of branches and leaves, as well as the closeness to the ground, afford considerable protection.

The more minute structural features of xerophytes are no less significant than are the more obvious characteristics. Commonly the epidermis is thick and highly cutinized, and often it is superficially coated with wax, resin, or varnish. In woody stems there is a prominent bark development, the cork layers, in particular, being of great significance in

Fig. 76.—*Agave Wightii.* A succulent xerophyte. (Photograph by William Trelease. Courtesy of Dr. George T. Moore and the Missouri Botanical Garden.)

checking transpiration. The leaf and stem surfaces frequently are covered with hairs, and spinescence is also common. Spinescence is of no significance in protection from transpiration but in some plants the spines probably do afford protection from herbivorous animals. Stomata occur only on protected surfaces, chiefly the undersides of leaves, and often are placed at the bases of pits or other depressions and may be further protected by hairs or heavy cutinization or both.

Many xerophytes are succulent (Fig. 76); many contain latex; and oils and resins often are abundantly developed. The osmotic pressure of the cell sap usually is very high, especially in woody plants and in plants of alkaline soils. Conducting tissues are well developed, as is lignification, and annual rings are prominent. Bast fibers and other mechanical elements reach their highest development in xerophytes. Among the most severe of xeric habitats are the alkali plains and basins where excessive climatic aridity is supplemented by a soil in which highly concentrated salts make absorption extremely difficult. Succulents with sap of high osmotic pressure seem to be best fitted for existence under such conditions but there are some places where the alkalinity is so great that plant life is practically excluded.

Some xerophytes, especially rock lichens, are entirely lacking in the ordinary xeric structures but are able to withstand prolonged desiccation and then quickly revive with the coming of rains. Aside from lichens and mosses absorption through aërial organs is relatively rare in xerophytes. Tubers, bulbs, and corms are especially characteristic of xeric habitats and are of great advantage because of their ability to develop rapidly at the beginning of a rainy season. Vegetative reproduction, however, is not prominent and the production of flowers and fruits is favored by xeric conditions.

108. **Plants of Habitats that are Physiologically Dry.**—Plants that grow in saline soil or in salty water are called halophytes and they are strikingly xeric. Perhaps the most characteristic feature of halophytes, as a group, is their succulence which is accompanied by very high osmotic pressure. We have already spoken of alkali plains, which are usually physically as well as physiologically dry, and we are concerned now only with those habitats which contain an abundance of water. The oceans are, of course, halic (characterized by physiological dryness) habitats but the majority of plants in them are algæ which are for the most part sub-

merged and, therefore, not subject to transpiration. Because of this protection from transpiration these algæ do not show xeric features.

Much more interesting from our point of view are the salt marshes which contain strikingly xeric plants comparable to those occurring on saline soils. In temperate

Fig. 77.—A mangrove thicket. Halic plants. (Photograph by H. L. Shantz. Courtesy of H. L. Shantz and the U. S. Department of Agriculture.)

regions the most representative salt-marsh plants are herbaceous, but in tropical and subtropical regions there are extensive mangrove forests occupying halic habitats. Few plants show more marked xeric features than the mangroves (Fig. 77). They have evergreen leaves which have water storage tissue, prominent palisade cells, and thick cutin. Often there is a network of roots extending from the branches down through the water and into the soil below.

Frequently, also, there are ascending "knees" comparable to those found in cypress swamps.

Another very interesting type of habitat which seems to be physiologically dry, although there is an abundance of water present, is the bog (Fig. 78). Bogs are formed in places where lack of drainage, and consequently lack of aëration, leads to an accumulation of carbon dioxide and of undecayed or only partly decayed organic matter. One

FIG. 78.—Cordova bog, Alaska. (Photograph by George B. Rigg.)

result of this is a rather high degree of acidity of the water. Possibly some other substances which may be somewhat toxic to the roots of plants also accumulate. The habitat is not well understood but it seems to be difficult for plants to absorb water from it and undoubtedly the acidity is one of the factors causing this. The peat moss (*Sphagnum*) is especially characteristic of bogs. There are also many orchids, insectivorous plants, and such woody plants as cranberry (*Vaccinium*), leather leaf (*Chamœdaphne*), bog rosemary (*Andromeda*), and tamarack trees (*Larix laricina*).

Many of these plants, especially the woody ones, show marked xeric features. Some of them, the tamarack for example, like many plants of saline habitats, grow better elsewhere if given a chance, indicating that they "tolerate" rather than "prefer" these physiologically dry habitats. This means only that, under ordinary conditions, they are not able to compete with other plants in more favorable habitats but are able to meet competition in the unfavorable ones.

109. Plants of Mesic Habitats. The most typical mesic habitats are found in deciduous forest regions. In many respects the structural characteristics of mesophytes are more or less strictly intermediate between those of the xerophytes and hydrophytes that we have discussed, but, of course, all degrees of gradation could be found between the few typical habitats with which we are dealing.

In the typical mesic habitats there is usually a prominent development of vertical roots with abundant root hairs. The foliage reaches a maximum development and the leaves are relatively large and thin. The thin, transparent layers of epidermis and an abundance of chlorophyll cause the leaves to appear dark green, in contrast to the pale green leaves characteristic of xeric plants. Stomata usually occur on both surfaces of the leaves, except in the case of trees where they ordinarily are on the lower surface only. The guard cells have a maximum capacity for movement and cutinization of walls is usually moderate.

110. The Life-forms of Raunkiaer.—Raunkiaer is a Danish botanist. His classification of plants into life-forms is the result of an attempt to find some method of estimating the relative values of the climates of various parts of the world by means of some standard that would have a direct bearing on plant life. The ordinary physical methods of measuring climatic influences are unsatisfactory because very different physical factors may have quite similar effects on plant growth and various combinations of factors may produce essentially the same growth-forms. The measurement of any single climatic factor or group of factors, therefore, does not give us an accurate estimate of the value of the climate for plant life.

For these reasons it was felt by Raunkiaer that the plants themselves should be the recorders of the biological value of any climate. The factor that was selected was the nature and degree of protection of the perennating bud or shoot apex during the critical season. A perennating bud is one that lives through a critical season and may develop into a shoot during the next growing season. It was necessary first of all, therefore, to classify plants on the basis of bud protection. The classification as finally used by Raunkiaer is as follows, the symbol used for each life form following the name in parentheses.

1. Stem succulents (S).

2. Epiphytes (E).

3. Megaphanerophytes and mesophanerophytes (MM). The megaphanerophytes are trees that are over 30 meters high while the mesophanerophytes are trees from 8 to 30 meters high. Since the buds are freely exposed in both they are grouped together.

4. Microphanerophytes (M). These are small trees and shrubs from 2 to 8 meters high.

5. Nanophanerophytes (N). Shrubs that are less than 2 meters high. All trees and shrubs may be spoken of simply as phanerophytes.

6. Chamaephytes (Ch). These are plants that have their buds or shoot apices perennating on the surface of the ground or just above it, so that in regions with snow they are protected during the winter and in regions with dry seasons some protection is afforded by plant remains. The buds are thus better protected than in phanerophytes. Plants with runners, cushion plants, etc., belong in this group.

7. Hemicryptophytes (H). These plants have dormant buds in the upper crust of the soil just below the surface.

14

The aërial parts of these plants are herbaceous and die down at the beginning of the critical season so that they form an additional protection. Most rosette plants belong here.

8. Geophytes (G). The geophytes have their dormant parts subterranean. They are plants with bulbs, rhizomes, tubers, etc.

9. Helophytes and hydrophytes (HH). The helophytes are marsh plants with their buds at the surface of the water or in the subjacent soil. The hydrophytes are water plants with perennating rhizomes or winter buds. It is unfortunate, of course, that the term hydrophyte is used here in a much narrower sense than ordinarily. The geophytes, helophytes and hydrophytes are collectively called cryptophytes.

10. Therophytes (Th). These are the plants which live through the critical season as seeds; that is, they are annual plants.

It is readily seen that this classification does not take into consideration any of the lower forms of plant life. It is further seen that, leaving out of consideration the first two groups, the stem succulents and epiphytes, which in a sense stand apart by themselves, the remaining groups, beginning with the phanerophytes in Group 3, form a series in which each type has its buds better protected than has the type preceding it. In using this classification for the evaluation of a climate the species of the flora are listed and the percentage of species falling in each group is determined. This list of percentages is spoken of as a biological spectrum and is compared with a normal spectrum which is supposed to represent the average conditions for the entire earth. The normal spectrum used by Raunkiaer is as follows:

S	E	MM	M	N	Ch	H	G	HH	Th
1	3	6	17	20	9	27	3	1	13

In comparing the biological spectrum of any region with the normal spectrum the important feature is the place of greatest deviation from the normal. For example, a study

that was made of the flora of New York and vicinity gave
the following spectrum.

S	E	MM	M	N	Ch	H	G	HH	Th
0	0	4.55	7.18	3.51	5.29	33.29	20.23	11.74	13

The greatest deviation from the normal in this spectrum
is found in the large percentage of geophytes and of helophytes
and hydrophytes. Since these three groups together are
called cryptophytes, the climate of the region may be called
a cryptophytic climate. Some other, rather incomplete,
studies that have been made in this country have indicated
that the climate of the plains region in the vicinity of Akron,
Colorado, is hemicryptophytic, that in Tooele Valley,
Utah, chamæphytic, and that of Death Valley, California,
therophytic.

111. **Vegetation Forms.**—A simple classification into vegetation forms which may be made to include the whole plant
kingdom is sometimes found useful. Such a classification,
based upon the methods of increase and the character and
length of life of the vegetative shoots, consists of four large
groups; namely, annuals, biennials, herbaceous perennials,
and woody perennials.

Annual plants pass the unfavorable season in the seed or
spore form, and the vegetative shoots live during only one
growing season, the entire length of life of the plant being
about one year. Biennials pass one unfavorable season as
seeds or spores and the next as a vegetative propagating
organ of some form. There is no accumulation of aërial
shoots and the plant lives during two or parts of two years.
Herbaceous perennials pass each unfavorable season both in
the seed or spore form and in the form of vegetative propagating parts. There is no accumulation of aërial shoots but
the plant lives several or many years. Woody perennials pass
each unfavorable season in the form of seeds or spores or
as plants with aërial shoots.

For more accurate description of vegetation types the last two groups, herbaceous perennials and woody perennials, may be subdivided as shown in the following list.

1. Annuals.
2. Biennials.
Herbaceous perennials.
3. Sod-grasses.
4. Bunch-grasses.
5. Bush-herbs.
6. Cushion-herbs.
7. Mat-herbs.
8. Rosette-herbs.
9. Carpet-herbs.
10. Succulents.
Woody perennials.
11. Half shrubs.
12. Bushes.
13. Succulents.
14. Shrubs.
15. Trees.

112. The Evolution of Growth-forms.—Our knowledge is not yet sufficient to enable us to arrange all of the growth-forms of plants in an evolutionary sequence which we can be sure is correct, and perhaps it never will be. But a beginning has been made by a number of workers, and it is now believed that among the angiosperms the woody type is more ancient than the herbaceous. Probably the most primitive type of tree is the sparingly branched, rain-forest type with large, undivided leaves. During the course of evolution more xeric forms have been produced and there has been a tendency toward reduction in size of plant and of leaf, an increase in the amount of branching of the plant and of the veins in the leaves, the production of compound leaves and of deciduous leaves, and the development of thorns and of succulence. Climbing plants, epiphytes, parasites, and herbaceous shade plants, all of which may occur in primitive habitats along with trees, are probably all much more recent than the trees. Probably all of the angiosperms of desert and semi-desert conditions are relatively recent. Extreme hydrophytes or aquatic plants are also thought to be derivative. The annual type of flowering plant is considered the most recent of all.

REFERENCES.

Bews, J. W.:   Plant Forms and Their Evolution in South Africa, Longmans, Green and Co., London, 1925, 199 p.

Cannon, William Austin: General and Physiological Features of the More Arid Portions of Southern Africa with Notes on the Climatic Environment, Carnegie Inst. Washington Publ., 1924, **354**, VIII + 159 p., 31 pl., 13 fig.

Emerson, Fred W.:   Subterranean Organs of Bog Plants, Bot. Gaz., 1921, **72**, 359–379, 11 fig.

Rigg, George B.:   A Summary of Bog Theories, Plant World, 1916, **19**, 310–325.

Shreve, Edith B.:   Seasonal Changes in the Water Relations of Desert Plants, Ecology, 1923, **4**, 266–292, fig. 1–11.

Skipper, E. G.:   The Ecology of the Gorse (Ulex) with Special Reference to the Growth-forms on the Hindhead Common, Jour. Ecol., 1922, **10**, 24–52, pl. 1., 9 fig.

Smith, William G.:   Raunkiaer's "Life-forms" and Statistical Methods, Jour. Ecol., 1913, **1**, 16–26.

CHAPTER XVI.

PLANT COMMUNITIES.

PLANTS do not ordinarily live alone like hermits but are found growing along with other plants in communities that usually consist of many individuals (Fig. 79). When an ecologist goes into a forest he does not see merely a number of trees, shrubs, and herbaceous plants with no relations one to another except that they happen to be growing in close proximity. What he sees is a plant community which is just as simple and understandable but with its multitude of activities just as complex, just as inevitable in its structural make-up but with its succession of life problems just as intensely interesting as any city or other community dominated by the genus of bipeds to which we belong.

The kinds of plants that one may expect to find in any community depend upon the factors of the environment, for just as we, in order to live and be healthy, must have homes that are adequately supplied with heat, light, water and food, so the plants in their homes are affected by these same factors of the environment. For this reason various kinds of plants that require the same type of environment are habitually found living together in the same community. So true is this that often when an experienced field man sees a certain species of plant he almost instinctively looks for other species that he has learned are usually associated with this one.

The ecology of plant communities is called synecology and will be discussed in this and the following six chapters.

113. The Plant Community an Organism.—The individual plants that make up a plant community are living together in a state of social disjunctive symbiosis but they are so intimately associated that the community as a whole may be considered as an organic entity; that is, an individual organism. Ecologists are by no means in complete agreement that

FIG. 79.—A plant community consisting of many individuals. (Photograph by William E. McQuiston.)

it should be so considered but we shall see that it is perfectly logical to do so. As an individual the plant community is born, it grows and develops, it matures, reproduces, and may finally die like any other organic individual.

If we consider the plant community as an individual organ-

ism then we recognize three distinct types of individuals.
The first of these is the single cell. This was the first kind
of individual that appeared on earth and at first, of course,
there was only the one type. The single cell performed all
of the functions that it is necessary for a plant to perform
and, of course, there was no such thing as division of labor.
After a while, however, some of these one-celled organisms
began to cling together and so form little colonies or communities of cells. They were still all alike, each one performing
all functions, but from these little colonies have evolved the
much larger communities of cells that we call the higher
plants and animals. Thus a higher plant, such as a spruce
tree (Fig. 80), is a community of millions of individuals of
the first type of which we have spoken. It is a representative of the second type of individual. In this individual,
which is really a community of cells, there is a decided
division of labor and a differentiation of form and structure
among the component individuals.

Just as the second type of individual is a community composed of individuals of the first type, so a plant community,
which we consider as the third type of individual, is composed
of individuals of the second type, largely, though some of
the component individuals may be of the first type. It is
a little difficult at first to think of a plant community as an
individual in the sense that a tree is an individual, because
we have not been in the habit of so considering it, but there
is no greater degree of difference between a tree and a plant
community, such as a forest, than there is between a tree
and a one-celled alga, and we shall find that the forest community has a life cycle and can do practically everything
that the tree can do.

In every plant community there are certain species of
plants that are called dominant plants because they largely
control the environment and so determine what other species
may grow in the community. In a forest the dominant
species are trees. They have very important symbiotic

relations with all other members of the community through their direct or indirect control of light, space relations, water supply, and to a certain extent available food materials. From this point of view it is of interest to compare a plant community with a human community. In a human com-

Fig. 80.—A black spruce tree, an individual of the second type which is composed of millions of cells or individuals of the first type. (Photograph by A. G. Eldredge.)

munity man is the dominant species. As the dominant species he controls the environment to such an extent as to determine what other species may live in the community. Some of the other species usually found in a human community are the horse, dog, cat, mouse, fly, etc. Some of these are not present because man wants them to be, but because man is present and is controlling the environment in such a way as to make it possible for the other species to live in the community. These facts are just as true of the plant community. The presence of some of the species is distinctly advantageous to the dominant plants, while that of others is just as distinctly disadvantageous, as for example the parasitic fungi, but they are all present because the dominant plants have made it possible by their control of the environment.

114. The Migration of Plants.—As we examine various plant communities growing in very different environments we are impressed by the fact that nearly all plants seem to be growing in places to which they are very well suited. Where did they all come from and how did they succeed in finding a congenial environment? The answer to this question is to be found largely in the efficient means that most plants have for disseminating their propagating bodies.

Fruits that open at maturity, such as capsules and pods, are called dehiscent fruits while those that do not open at maturity, such as berries and akenes, are called indehiscent. In the case of plants with indehiscent fruits usually the entire fruits are disseminated while plants with dehiscent fruits commonly scatter the seeds only. In some plants the seeds are forcibly expelled by the act of dehiscence. The seeds of the violet and of the lupine are thus hurled out to a distance of several decimeters and those of the witch hazel are often scattered for several meters. In the *Geranium* the carpels separate from the base of the main axis of the fruit and curl upward with such suddenness as to discharge the seeds. In the touch-me-not (*Impatiens*) the mature fruit is under such tension that a mere touch causes it to dehisce violently and so scatter the seeds. The fruits of the dwarf mistletoe (*Arceuthobium*) explode at maturity and hurl the seeds for several meters, and, since the seeds are sticky, they readily adhere to the bark of trees on which the mistletoe is parasitic.

Many capsules and pods do not dehisce violently but open up and remain in such a position that their seeds are easily shaken out by wind or brushed out by animals. In many mints the nutlets may be shot out if the calyx is pressed down and then released, and in the smartweed (*Polygonum virginianum*) the akene is attached to an elastic cushion in such a way that when it is pressed back and then released it bounds off to a distance of two or three meters. These means of dissemination are of course relatively inefficient because the seeds are never scattered more than a few meters from the parent plant.

The spores of many fungi are forcibly discharged at maturity. The fungus *Pilobolus* grows only on dung piles and when the spores are mature they are discharged in masses which usually fall on the grass or other vegetation surrounding the dung pile. They can never germinate and grow on the grass but if the grass is eaten by an animal the spores pass through the alimentary canal and are deposited in a suitable substratum for germination and growth. The spores of many Ascomycetes and Basidiomycetes are discharged into the air and are then caught by air currents and carried away.

Many plants with rhizomes or runners depend more upon growth than upon the dissemination of seeds or fruits for migration. Migration by growth is a very slow but otherwise efficient means of advance into new territory.

115. **Migration Through the Aid of Wind.**—Wind is probably the most efficient of disseminating agents, at least as to the numbers of seeds or spores carried. Spores being lighter than seeds are often carried much further, though very small seeds, such as those of orchids, may be carried for great distances.

Many adaptations for wind dissemination are found. In the maple (*Acer*), the hop tree (*Ptelea*), and the elm (*Ulmus*) the fruits, called samaras, are provided with wing-like appendages which often contain air spaces of considerable size. These prevent the fruits from falling rapidly to the ground. The seeds of *Catalpa* are similarly provided with wings. Very characteristic wind-scattered fruits are found

in many members of the composite family.   In the dandelion, for example, the involucre closes after the flowers have
bloomed, remains closed while the fruits are maturing, and
opens again when the fruits are ready for dissemination.
Each fruit is provided with a crown of hairs, the pappus,
which spreads out like a parachute and prevents the fruit
from falling quickly while being carried by air currents.
In the milkweeds (*Asclepias*), the willows (*Salix*), and the
poplars (*Populus*), the seeds are provided with tufts of hairs
which render them as well adapted to wind dissemination
as are the akenes of the dandelion and other composites.
The abundant hairs on the seeds of the cotton plant (*Gos-
sypium*) are, from the point of view of the plant, an adaptation for wind dissemination.   Somewhat similar cottony
hairs are found on the seeds of some of the anemones and
of the cotton grass (*Eriophorum*).

Remarkably interesting adaptations for wind dissemination are found in the so-called tumble weeds.   These are
plants which, at maturity, break off from the roots and are
tumbled along over the ground by the wind, scattering their
seeds as they go.   In the case of the Russian thistle (*Salsola
Kali tenuifolia*) and the tumble weed amaranth (*Amaranthus
græcizans*) the entire shoot breaks off at the surface of the
soil, while in the old witch grass (*Panicum capillary*) only
the panicle breaks off.   Sometimes the panicles of old witch
grass become attached to other tumble weeds and are carried
along with them.

Many kinds of bacteria and the spores of lower plants are
scattered principally by the wind.   Samples of air taken
almost anywhere at any time are found to contain greater
or smaller numbers of these minute organisms.

116. **Migration Through the Aid of Water.**—Water is less
efficient than wind as far as the numbers of propagating bodies
carried are concerned, but it is an important disseminating
agent largely because it may carry fruits or seeds for long
distances.   In streams and ocean currents the propagating

bodies are all carried in a definite direction but in lakes and ponds the direction often varies with the changing direction of the wind.

All seeds are heavier than air and therefore the distance to which they can be carried in that medium is necessarily limited. Many seeds and fruits, however, are lighter than water and so may float almost indefinitely. This is especially true of the fruits of many water plants which often have large air spaces in the ovary walls or the seed coats. The seeds of many land plants, however, sink in water, some quickly and others after a longer time, so that the distance to which they may be carried is limited. The length of time that a seed may float on water and still be viable is closely connected with its resistance to the infiltration of water. Many seeds that are capable of floating rather quickly lose their ability to germinate because of the entrance of water which institutes decay. This is likely to be especially true if the water is rough and still more so if it is salty as well as rough. For example, the cocoanut, which is often seen floating on tropical waters, has frequently been cited as a typical example of water dispersal to distant islands. This fruit, however, usually loses its viability within a few days through the infiltration of water so that it is doubtful whether it could populate a very distant land unless it were carried on driftwood or by some comparable means. On the other hand, there are some fruits and seeds that can float on water for a very long time without becoming injured. The fruits of *Suriana maritima*, a common tropical plant, have been shown by experiment to be uninjured after floating on rough, salty water for one hundred and forty-three days, and the seeds of *Hibiscus tiliaceus* were viable after floating in a similar way for one hundred and twenty-one days. The seeds of some species of *Asparagus* may be viable after soaking in water for a year, and those of the arrow-leaf (*Sagittaria*) and of the mermaid-weed (*Proserpinaca*) have been shown to be uninjured after soaking at the bottom of a pond for seven years.

Fruits and seeds are often carried great distances on drift-wood or other articles floating on water. Furthermore the seedlings of some kinds of plants may float for days on water and then, if stranded in a suitable place, take root and grow. The seedlings of some species of bur marigold (*Bidens*) are sometimes seen floating on water by the hundreds and many of them later succeed in finding suitable places to grow. In the case of duckweeds and many algæ the mature plants float on water and may be carried from place to place.

117. **Migration Through the Aid of Animals.**—Many inde-hiscent fruits, especially bur fruits and others that have hooked appendages, are involuntarily distributed by animals. The cocklebur (*Xanthium*), burdock (*Arctium*), bur mari-gold (*Bidens*), hound's tongue (*Cynoglossum*), sweet cicely (*Osmorhiza*), bed-straw (*Galium*), beggar's lice (*Lappula*), and bur grass (*Cenchrus*) are familiar examples of animal disseminated fruits.

Another interesting class of fruits that are scattered by animals consists of those that are fleshy or possess a more or less juicy, edible pulp. Such fruits are eaten abundantly by birds and other animals and the seeds are likely to be disseminated. On the other hand, fruit-eating animals do not always facilitate dispersal, since they eat and digest many seeds. Acorns and nuts of various kinds are eaten in large quantities by squirrels. Occasionally nuts that are buried by squirrels are not eaten and so may germinate, but as a means of dissemination this method is, to say the least, very precarious. Ants are dissemination agents of consider-able importance in the case of seeds, such as those of blood-root (*Sanguinaria*), ginger (*Asarum*), and the false mermaid weed (*Flœrkia*), which have oily or albuminous appendages. The ants feed upon these appendages and often carry the seeds considerable distances.

Wading birds often carry seeds in the mud that adheres to their feet. This undoubtedly accounts for the wide distribution of many aquatic plants since such birds often fly for great distances and almost always from one body of water to another. The efficiency of animals as disseminating agents lies primarily in the fact that each species of animal frequents the same type of vegetation most of the time. Animals that live in forests, for example, either stay in the same forest or go from one forest to another so that any seeds or fruits that they carry are likely to be dropped in places that are suitable for their growth.

Man is a very important agent of dispersal. He acts in the same way as other animals to a certain extent but is more important because of his common carriers. Railroad trains, for example, may carry seeds for long distances and scatter them along the right of way. So true is this that one almost always finds a flora along a railroad that is rich in the number of species.

118. **Plant Succession.**—The discussion of the means of dissemination in the preceding paragraphs is enough to answer the question as to where the plants that we see came from and how they happened to find suitable places in which to grow. They came from already existing communities and the seeds of each species were scattered everywhere, but only those that fell into suitable communities were able to grow. The development of plant communities from birth to maturity is called plant succession. This will be discussed at length in later chapters but it will aid us in grasping the significance of the individuality of plant communities if we trace briefly the development of one at this time.

Let us take for example a beech and maple forest such as may be found in Indiana or Ohio as well as in a number of the other states east of the Mississippi River. Let us suppose that after the glacial period an area of bare rock of fairly high elevation was left exposed somewhere in Indiana or eastern Illinois. The bare rock was, of course, not a suitable place for trees to grow, but, since it was a bare area, that is, an area unoccupied by plants, it was a good place for the birth of a plant community. The first plants that appeared on the rock were some xeric lichens. This was the birth or beginning of the new plant community.

The lichens grew very slowly, but gradually they eroded the surface of the rock, causing it to crumble somewhat, and they also collected dust and other materials blown upon the rock by the wind, so that after a number of years they had formed a small amount of soil upon the rock. Because of this soil, which would hold a certain amount of moisture, it was now possible for a few kinds of mosses to grow here. With the coming of the mosses the formation of soil went on more rapidly and some years later, therefore, it was possible for some of the more xeric herbaceous plants to come in. Probably the first ones were some of the common weeds and these were later followed by grasses and the perennial plants that usually grow along with the grasses. Notice, now, that as more plants grew here and more soil was formed the place was becoming less and less xeric. Finally, after many years, there was soil enough and water enough that woody plants began to appear. Perhaps the first was the juniper, or some xeric shrubs, but later other and larger trees came, especially the black and white oaks and the hickories. Our plant community had now developed into a real forest and, because of the shade and the increasing layer of leaf mold, it was becoming quite mesic but it was still too dry for the beech and maple for these trees are confirmed mesophytes. Of course the oaks and hickories had many other trees, shrubs, and herbaceous plants associated with them, each of which had its part to play in the community, and they flourished for many years. But gradually the place became more and more mesic, the oaks and hickories gave place to the beeches and maples, and the community had at last reached its maturity (Fig. 81).

We shall see that the development of such a community is just as definite as is that of any other type of individual. In other words, it was just as certain that this would in time develop into a beech-maple forest and not into some other kind of community as it is that an acorn will develop into an oak tree and not into a hickory or some other kind of tree.

119. **A Tree and a Plant Community Compared.**—We have stated that a plant community is born, it grows and develops, matures, reproduces, and may die, like any other individual. It will be profitable now, before taking up the details of the structure of plant communities, to compare the life cycle of

FIG. 81.—A mature forest community of birch, beech, maple and hemlock. (Photograph by A. G. Varela. Courtesy of H. L. Shantz and the U. S. Department of Agriculture.)

a plant community with that of a tree (a cell community). In order to make the comparison less abstract we will compare a beech-maple community with an oak tree.

A plant community always starts on some kind of a bare area and a bare rock surface will serve as well as any. This bare area then represents a sort of potential plant succession —a possible place for the birth of a plant community. But a plant community will never develop here until something comes in from the outside. Turning to the oak tree we may

15

compare the egg cell before fertilization with a bare area.
It represents a potential plant; but it will never develop
until something, the male gamete, comes into it from the
outside.

We are using birth here only in the sense of a beginning or
an origin. Therefore, we may take the fertilized egg (a
single cell) as the beginning or birth of the new individual
that is to develop into an oak tree. Corresponding to this
on the bare area we would have first a single crustose lichen.
In order that these young organisms may grow they must both
receive something more from the outside. The fertilized
egg must receive food and the young community must receive
plants. The fertilized egg now develops into an embryo,
and the young community develops into a lichen-moss
community; the embryo develops into a seedling, and the
lichen-moss community develops into a perennial herbaceous
plant community; the seedling develops into a shrub, and
the perennial herbaceous plant community develops into a
shrub community; the shrub develops into a sapling, and the
shrub community develops into a xeric tree (oak-hickory)
community. These are mere progressive steps in the development of these two organisms. The sapling now matures
into a tree, and the xeric tree community matures into a
mesic tree (beech-maple) community.

The mature oak tree, which is a representative of the second
type of individual, is a community of individuals of the first
type, and it reproduces by giving off single individuals of
the first type (cells or gametes). The plant community,
on the other hand, is a community of individuals of the second
type, and it reproduces by giving off single individuals of the
second type (plants, usually in seeds). As to death, there
seems to be no reason why a tree should ever die unless it
gets diseased or meets with an accident. Some of the big
trees of California have lived for several thousand years and
there is no reason to suppose that they will not keep on living,
unless they become diseased or meet with an accident.

The same thing may be said of a plant community. It may die from disease or from an accident, but otherwise it will continue to live indefinitely. It is a little hard at first to visualize the phenomena concerned with this third type of organism only because we have not been used to doing so. It is necessary to keep in mind the bigness of these organisms and of the phenomena concerned and to learn to think in terms of bigness. For example, some organisms of the first type (bacteria) may complete their life cycles in a half-hour, for some of those of the second type (a tree) it may take a hundred years, but for those of the third type (a plant community) it may, in some cases, take a million years. The following tabular comparison may help to make clear the comparison discussed above.

	Oak tree	Beech-maple community
Bare area	Egg cell	Bare rock
Birth	Fertilized egg	Crustose lichen
Growth and	(Take in food)	(Take in plants)
Development	Embryo	Lichen-Moss Community
	Seedling	Herbaceous plant community
	Shrub	Shrub community
	Sapling	Xeric tree community
		(Oaks and hickories)
Maturity	Oak tree	Mesic tree community
		(Beech and maple)
Reproduction	Gives off cells	Gives off plants (seeds)
Death	From disease or accident	From disease or accident

REFERENCES.

Gardner, Max W.: The Mode of Dissemination of Fungus and Bacterial Diseases of Plants, Report Michigan Acad. Sci., 1918, **20**, 357–423.

Gleason, H. A.: The Individualistic Concept of the Plant Association, Bull. Torrey Bot. Club., 1926, **53**, 7–26.

Gleason, H. A.: The Vegetational History of the Middle West, Ann. Assn. Am. Geogr., 1923, **12**, 39–85.

Heald, F. D., Gardner, M. W. and Studhalter, R. A.: Air and Wind Dissemination of Ascospores of the Chestnut Blight Fungus, Jour. Agr. Res., 1915, **3**, 493–526.

Howell, A. Brazier: Agencies which Govern the Distribution of Life, Am. Nat., 1922, **56**, 428–438.

Phillips, E. P.: Adaptation for the Dispersal of Fruits and Seeds, South African Jour. Nat. Hist., 1920, **2**, 240–252, pl. 2–3.

Shull, G. H.: The Longevity of Submerged Seeds, Plant World, 1914, **17**, 329–337.

Small, James: The Origin and Development of the Compositæ, Chapter IX. Fruit Dispersal. New Phytol., 1918, **17**, 200–230.

CHAPTER XVII.

THE STRUCTURE OF PLANT ASSOCIATIONS.

A ONE-CELLED plant, or individual of the first type as described in the preceding chapter, has certain definite morphological parts which are usually readily recognized and to which names are applied. The cell wall, cytoplasm, nucleus, and nucleolus are such parts. Likewise an oak tree, or individual of the second type, has easily distinguishable morphological parts such as roots, stems, and leaves. We may reasonably expect, therefore, to find somewhat comparable structural parts in the case of an individual of the third type, the plant community. This we shall be able to do, but, just as leaves, stems or roots may be so reduced or so modified that they are very difficult to recognize, so the structural parts of a plant community, while very readily recognized in many cases, are often so reduced or modified that their recognition is by no means easy.

120. **Plant Associations.**—An individual plant community is called a plant association. A plant association, therefore, is an individual of the third type, just as a plant is an individual of the second type, and a cell an individual of the first type.

As stated in the preceding chapter, there are in each plant association certain species of plants that are called dominant species because they in a large measure exert a controlling influence upon the environment. There may be only a single dominant species or there may be several and the other species that are growing along with the dominant plants are called secondary species. The associations are named from the dominant species. Thus we may speak of the sage brush association, meaning an association in which sage brush is dominant, or we may speak of an oak-hickory association (Fig. 82), or of a beech-maple-hemlock association. The scientific names of the dominant plants may be used instead of the common names, as, for example, the *Artemisia* association, the *Acer saccharum* association, or the *Quercus-Carya* association.

Fig. 82.—An oak-hickory association.

The term, plant association, may be used in either the concrete or the abstract sense. For example, we may speak of a particular plant community as an oak-hickory association in which case we would be using the term in the concrete sense, or we may say that the oak-hickory association is characteristic of the drier uplands throughout Indiana in which case we are using it in the abstract sense. This practice is, of course, no different than the common usage of the names of individual plants. In speaking of an individual tree, for instance, we may say that it is a white oak, using the name in the concrete sense, but if we say that the white oak is common in eastern Illinois we are using the same name in an abstract sense.

A plant association, viewed in the concrete, may be defined as a plant community characterized by its essentially homogeneous physiognomy and ecological structure and by its essentially homogeneous floristic composition, at least with regard to dominant species. In the abstract the association may be defined as a vegetation-unit characterized by an essentially constant physiognomy and ecological structure and by an essentially constant floristic composition, at least with regard to dominant species.

Physiognomy, as used in the above definitions, refers to the general outward appearance, or external morphology of the association. This is determined almost entirely by the nature of the more prominent plants that enter into its structural composition and more particularly by the nature and abundance of the dominant species. Thus, when we refer to an association as deciduous forest, or evergreen forest, or prairie, we are speaking in terms of physiognomy.

Ecological structure includes all peculiarities of vegetation that are of ecological significance. It is to the plant association what morphological and physiological structure are to a plant. It takes into consideration not only those peculiarities that are visibly expressed in the growth forms of the plants but also those that are not so expressed. For example, the behavior of the various plants that make up the association in relation to various conditions of light, heat, water, soil, and other factors of the environment would be included under ecological structure. Thus, when we speak of plants as being xeric, hydric, or mesic, or when we speak of them as being tolerant or intolerant of shade we are speaking of characteristics that come under the head of ecological structure but which may or may not be expressed in the growth forms of the plants. Furthermore, while physiognomy is concerned primarily with the dominant species only, ecological structure takes into consideration all of the secondary plants as well.

Floristic composition refers, of course, to the species of plants that make up the association, but it is the relatively common and conspicuous species, that is, the dominant species, that are of most importance.

Fig. 83.—Yellow pine consociation in a yellow pine-douglas fir association. (Photograph by A. G. Varela. Courtesy of H. L. Shantz and the U. S. Department of Agriculture.)

121. Consociations.—A consociation is a morphological part of a plant association and is characterized by having a single dominant species (Fig. 83). There are as many consociations in each association, therefore, as there are dominant species. If the association has but one dominant species the single consociation is coextensive with the entire association. In many cases also the dominant species are mixed throughout the association and therefore the consociations are mixed and are coextensive with the association as well as with one another. In all of these cases, however, there is no practical reason for recognizing consociations at all and it is probably better, on the whole, not to do so. The recognition of consociations becomes of value, however, in case a part of an association is dominated by a single species to the exclusion of other dominants. For example, in an upland oak-hickory association in which the dominant species are white oak, black oak, and shag-bark hickory, we may find a portion of the community in which the white oak is the only dominant that is present and it becomes convenient in such a case to speak of this morphological part of the association as a white oak consociation.

It should be understood that when we say a consociation is characterized by a single dominant we do not mean that it consists of the dominant species only. It consists of the dominant species and all of the secondary species that occur along with the dominants. That is, just as an association is made up of all of the dominant and secondary plants that are growing in the community, so the white oak consociation mentioned above would consist of all of the plants that were living in that part of the association dominated by white oak alone.

122. **Societies.**—A plant society is a morphological part of an association characterized by one or more subdominant species (Fig. 84). A subdominant species is one that exerts a measure of control over a portion of an association where, of course, the environment is already controlled by the true dominants. It is thus a dominance within a dominance. More often it is the aspect rather than the environment as such that is controlled by the subdominant species. The growth habits of the subdominants are ordinarily different from those of the dominants. For example, in a forest, where the dominant species are trees, the subdominant species are shrubs, herbs, or cryptogamic plants, and in a

125. Edaphic Climax Associations—In every climatic region there are some associations that have virtually reached maturity but which are not composed of the most mesic vegetation that the climate will support. A bottomland forest along a river (Fig. 86), for example, develops to a stage that is more hydric than the climatic climax but which, for all practical purposes and unless an extremely long time is allowed, will develop no further. It is prevented from developing further by the local soil conditions and for this reason may be called an edaphic climax association. Thus, if we define the climatic climax as the most mesic vegetation that the climate will support, the edaphic climax may be defined as the most mesic vegetation that the edaphic conditions will permit the climate to support.

REFERENCES.

Clements, Frederic E.: Plant Succession. An Analysis of the Development of Vegetation. Chapter VII. Structure and Units of Vegetation, Carnegie Inst. Washington, Pub. No. 242, 1916.

Gleason, Henry Allen: The Structure and Development of the Plant Association, Bull. Torrey Bot. Club, 1917, **43**, 463–481.

Nichols, George E.: A Working Basis for the Ecological Classification of Plant Communities, Ecology, 1923, **4**, 11–23; 154–179.

Tansley, Arthur George: Practical Ecology. A Guide for Beginners in Field Study of Plant Communities, Dodd, Mead and Co., New York, 1923.

CHAPTER XVIII.

THE CLASSIFICATION OF PLANT COMMUNITIES.

In dealing with any group of objects, living or otherwise, it is often convenient, or even necessary, to classify them in some logical way. The particular kind of classification that is best depends largely upon the use that is to be made of it. For example, we may classify seed plants according to growth form, or on the basis of relation to water supply, or into natural families and orders, and each of these classifications has valuable uses.

There has been a considerable amount of discussion and disagreement among ecologists concerning what is the best scheme of classification of plant communities. If, however, we recognize that plant associations are individuals we should be able to classify them in any way that may suit our purpose, just as we do in the case of individual plants, without being subjected to undue criticism. Some of the classifications that have been found useful by various workers will be discussed in this chapter.

126. **Habitats.**—Since some classifications of associations are based in part on habitat relations it is necessary to understand what is meant by habitat before taking up the discussion of classification. By the habitat of a plant or plant association is meant the kind of situation in which the organism lives. It is practically equivalent to what would be meant by the immediate environment. It is the place of abode of the organism together with all the environmental factors that are operative within the abode. The term may be applied to any area which is characterized by uniformity of at least some environmental conditions, such as a ravine, a bog, or a south-facing slope (Fig. 87).

(238)

It is necessary to distinguish between the habitat of the association and the habitats of the constituent plants that make up the association, for each growth-form within the association has a habitat that is different from that of every other growth-form. In a forest association, for example, the

Fig. 87.—A rock-ravine habitat. (Photograph by A. G. Eldredge.)

habitat of a subdominant shrub and that of a moss at the base of a tree are both quite different from the habitat of the dominant trees.

The factors that are operative within the habitat are very numerous and we will not attempt to present a complete list of them but will mention briefly some of the more important ones. Most of the habitat factors can be classed as either climatic, physiographic, or biotic.

Climatic Factors.—Climatic factors are those that are associated with atmospheric conditions, chiefly conditions of moisture, temperature, and light. Some of the climatic factors are regional or wide-spread in their effects. These are the ordinary factors of climate upon which the climatic regions of the earth are based. Others are quite local. Probably no two places on the surface of the earth have exactly the same climate though they may be very similar. Local differences in climate that are quite marked, however, are frequent, as, for example, the climate of a north-facing slope as compared with that of one facing south, or the climate of a ravine as compared with that of the adjacent upland.

Physiographic Factors.—Physiographic factors are those that are associated with peculiarities or variations in the form, structure, and behavior of the earth's surface. Slope, or the degree to which the surface of land departs from the level, is usually one of the most noticeable of the physiographic factors, but there are many others. Those that have to do with local variations in soil relations are called edaphic factors. These include the physical and chemical composition of the soil or other substratum, the degree of acidity or alkalinity, etc. Physiographic factors which change the local conditions, such as erosion, soil leaching, land-slides, etc., are also of very great importance.

Biotic Factors.—Biotic factors are those that are associated with the activities of plants and animals. Many of these have been discussed in the chapters on symbiosis and only a few will be mentioned here as examples. Shade, although it may be produced by other than living agencies, is usually a biotic factor. It increases atmospheric humidity and decreases transpiration and soil water evaporation, modifies both air and soil temperatures, prevents the growth of light-requiring plants, and favors the growth of shade-tolerant plants. The competition of plants for light, for water, or for mineral nutrients, is often a biotic factor of great importance. Humus, which is produced through the decay of dead plants and animals, affects the water relations, the aëration, the food supply, the temperature, the acidity, and the microscopic flora and fauna of the habitat. Parasitic and other symbiotic phenomena are so numerous that they cannot be taken up here. Man through his influence on the habitat is an extremely important biotic factor. Such activities as lumbering (Fig. 88), forest management, clearing

Fig. 88.—A forest partly destroyed through the lumbering activity of man.

land for agriculture, irrigation, cultivation of the soil, the introduction of grazing animals, etc., are examples of such influence.

127. **Physiographic Plant Formations.**—A group of associations within any geographically-defined area which one desires to classify together may be called a plant formation. One method by which the associations may be conveniently grouped is based on their relations to physiographic unit-areas. Physiographic unit-areas have reference to the larger and more outstanding features of the topography of a region

16

such as ravines, valleys (Fig. 89), uplands, lakes, bogs, swamps, etc. (Fig. 90).

FIG. 89.—The plant associations in this valley may be grouped together to form a physiographic plant formation. Photograph taken while a storm was in progress in the distance.

FIG. 90.—A physiographic unit-area occupied by a physiographic plant formation. (Photograph by A. G. Eldredge.)

In each physiographic unit-area there are certain habitat factors that prevail more or less uniformly throughout. For example, a ravine may be characterized by relatively high atmospheric humidity and by protection from sun and wind, a lake or swamp is characterized by the presence of abundant water, and an upland may be characterized by a relatively low soil-water content and perhaps by a particular type of soil   On the other hand, an area that is recognized as a physiographic unit ordinarily is not uniform throughout with respect to all of its habitat factors.   A rock ravine, for instance, may contain all variations from dry cliffs to very wet soil.   Thus such a physiographic unit represents a complex of distinct habitats and each habitat supports a separate association.

The entire complex of associations of a physiographic unit-area may be called a physiographic plant formation.   Such formations may be named and referred to in terms of physiography.   Thus we may speak of a valley formation, a rocky upland formation, or a bog formation.   These formations may be considered either in the concrete or in the abstract sense just as is true of the individual associations.   For example, we may refer concretely to the vegetation of a particular bog as a bog formation or we may speak abstractly of the bog formation of southern Michigan.

Usually the recognition of physiographic unit-areas in the field is not a difficult matter.   It is scarcely necessary nor desirable to make any definite rules to govern particular cases because our purpose is not always exactly the same. Sometimes we may find it convenient to place more emphasis upon edaphic conditions than upon topographic features in delimiting our physiographic formations.   Sometimes we may want to make use of rather large and comprehensive physiographic units and at other times smaller and more limited ones.   We must remember that it is always the vegetation rather than the physiography in which we are primarily interested, and since a formation is merely a group of plant associations the delimitation of our groups should depend, in part at least, upon our purpose in making the classification.

128. Climatic Plant Formations.—The climate in different places on the surface of the earth differs greatly because of varying distances from the equator, the relation to large bodies of water and to mountain ranges, the direction of the prevailing winds, the altitude, etc. Any portion of the earth's surface that is characterized by having essentially the same kind of climate throughout may be called a climatic unit-area. For example, a considerable portion of the northeast quarter of the United States is characterized by a temperate, damp climate which supports deciduous forest vegetation, the central part of the country has a drier climate which supports grassland vegetation, while much of the southwestern part is characterized by a desert climate and supports a desert type of vegetation. Each of these regions may be considered a climatic unit-area, and there are, of course, several other smaller units within the United States.

All of the vegetation within a climatic unit-area, taken in its entirety, may be called a climatic plant formation. Such a formation includes, as a rule, a very large number of associations and usually is made up of a number of physiographic formations. The associations within such a formation form a very heterogeneous complex but all of them are either representatives of the climatic climax vegetation of the region or they are developmental stages of the climax association. A climatic formation is usually named from its climax vegetation. Thus we may speak of the deciduous forest formation of the eastern United States, the grassland formation of the great plains region, or the desert formation of the southwestern part of the country. These climatic formations like associations and physiographic formations, may be referred to either in the concrete or in the abstract sense.

129. Association Types.—The two kinds of plant formations discussed above comprise all of the vegetation within geographically limited areas, and they necessarily contain associations that differ very greatly from one another because they are in different stages of development and are occupying different kinds of habitats. Frequently it is convenient to group together only those associations that are similar in physiognomy and ecological structure. Such a group may be called an association type. The association type, therefore, may be defined as a group of associations which resemble one another in physiognomy and ecological structure but which may differ in a greater or less degree in floristic composition. For example, upland deciduous forests all have about the same general appearance wherever they occur. They are essentially similar in physiognomy and ecological structure, though they may differ markedly in floristic composition. Such forest associations may all be grouped together in one association type.

It will be noted that the association types are characterized by rather obvious peculiarities of external appearance while the individual associations comprising them are distinguished from one another on the basis of floristic composition. For this reason it is usually the association types rather than the associations that we recognize as we look from the window of a moving train or from a speeding automobile. It is also the association types rather than the associations that first impress themselves upon us when we visit a region that is unfamiliar from the floristic point of view. We can readily describe the vegetation of a region in terms of association types without knowing any of the plants by name, but we cannot describe it in terms of the associations until we know the specific identity of at least the principal elements of the flora.

Association types are usually named according to their physiognomy and ecological structure. Thus we may speak of the xeric evergreen forest association type, the short grass prairie association type, the desert shrub association type, or the floating leaf association type.

In some cases there would seem to be some difficulty in distinguishing between association types and associations considered in the abstract. It must be remembered, however, that associations in order to be considered the same in the abstract sense must be essentially the same in floristic composition. We may speak, for example, of the beech-maple association of the eastern United States including in this abstract conception all associations of this region that have beech and maple as the dominant species, but we could not include any forest associations of Europe because they would be floristically different. On the other hand there are deciduous forest associations in Europe that are very similar in physiognomy and ecological structure to those of the United States, although they have nothing in common floristically, and those in the two countries may be grouped together in the same association type.

130. **Successional Series of Associations.**—Of the three kinds of classifications already discussed, the two types of plant formations, physiographic and climatic, are readily recognized because they are limited to certain geographic areas and contain all of the vegetation within those areas, while the association types are as readily recognized because of their similarity of physiognomy and ecological structure. The vegetation of a region cannot be thoroughly studied, however, without taking into consideration the dynamic or developmental phenomena. For this reason it is necessary sooner or later to classify the plant associations according to their genetic relationships. This is often much more difficult than classifying them according to formations or association types because it involves determining the relative maturity of each association and this frequently cannot be done by observation alone.

The phenomenon that furnishes a basis for a genetic classification of plant communities is plant succession. This process has been briefly outlined in Chapter XVI and will be discussed in more detail in Chapters XIX and XX. The development of a climax association from its beginning on a bare area results in an orderly sequence of associations, each member of the series being replaced by a more mature community until the climax is reached. This is brought about through a progressive change in the habitat due largely to the reactions of the vegetation upon the environment. All of the associations concerned in the development of a climax from beginning to maturity may be grouped together into a successional series or, as it is sometimes called, a sere. Usually in every region some examples of all of the developmental stages may be found so that by careful study it is possible to group them in their proper genetic relationships.

Several types of successional series or seres may be recognized on the basis of their origin. A sere always starts on a

FIG. 91.—Ruderal plants on a secondary bare area. The first stage of a mesarch secondary sere.

bare area. A bare area may be either primary or secondary. A primary bare area is one which has not supported plant life before and so contains no plant parts or remains, either living or dead. The substratum of a primary bare area is usually clay, sand, rock, or water. A secondary bare area, on the other hand, is one on which the plant community has been destroyed by one means or another. On such an area there is almost certain to be some humus and there may be seeds or other propagating organs that are alive. Any bare area is almost certain to be either wetter or drier than the habitat of the climax association. If it is wetter than the climax the succession will in general progress from hydric toward mesic. Such a successional series is said to be hydrarch. On the other hand, if the bare area is drier than the climax the succession progresses from xeric toward mesic and the successional series is said to be xerarch. A successional series or sere that starts on a primary clay area is called a geosere, one that starts on a primary sand area is called a psammosere, one that has its origin on bare rock is called a lithosere, and one that starts in water is called a hydrosere. Secondary successions sometimes begin in areas that are already mesic and develop rather quickly to the climax. Such seres are said to be mesarch (Fig. 91). These facts lead to the following classification of seres.

Primary seres:
> Hydrarch:
>> Geosere
>> Psammosere
>> Lithosere
>> Hydrosere

> Xerarch:
>> Geosere
>> Psammosere
>> Lithosere

Secondary seres:
> Hydrarch
> Xerarch
> Mesarch

REFERENCES.

Nichols, George E.: The Interpretation of Certain Terms and Concepts in the Ecological Classification of Plant Communities, Plant World, 1917, **20**, 305–317, 341–353.

Tansley, A. H.: The Classification of Vegetation and the Concept of Development, Jour. Ecology, 1920, **8**, 118–149.

Yapp, R. H.: The Concept of Habitat, Jour. Ecology, 1922, **10**, 1–17.

CHAPTER XIX.

PLANT SUCCESSION.

PLANT succession is a universal process by which all plant associations develop from beginnings on bare areas to maturity. As a general rule succession is from xerism toward mesism or from hydrism toward mesism. This is necessarily true because the mature, or climatic climax, vegetation is the most mesic that the climate can permanently support. There are some exceptions to the general rule, however. For example, in a region where the climax is a xeric type of vegetation, a sere that starts in water, as at the edge of an ox-bow lake or other inland depression, may develop progressively from a hydric condition to the xeric climax but in so doing it would necessarily pass through a mesic stage so that the last part of the sere would be from mesism toward xerism. We may say, therefore, that developmental plant succession always proceeds toward the climax and usually, though not necessarily, toward mesism.

More often, when succession is away from, rather than toward, mesism it is also away from the climax and is destructive rather than developmental in nature. For this reason it is necessary to distinguish between development and succession, or rather between developmental succession and succession that is not developmental. Succession that is not developmental is in general due to some change in the habitat that makes it less mesic. Such a change may take place rapidly or it may take place very slowly. In any case it is destructive in its effect since it cuts back the association to a younger stage. It is comparable to cutting back a tree, such as a willow, and so making a shrub of it. If such a willow tree, after it is cut back, is left undisturbed it will proceed at once to grow up again into a tree. Likewise, when a plant association is cut back to a younger stage by some means and then the cause ceases to act, developmental succession begins at once and proceeds toward the climax. The cutting back process, or succession away from the climax, has been called retrogression by some ecologists.

FIG. 92.—A bare area of shale produced by the erosive action of water.

131. Bare Areas.—A sere always starts on a bare area. Bare areas may be produced in a variety of ways. For example, erosion by the action of water may produce an area that is entirely without plants (Fig. 92). This frequently takes place at the upper end of a ravine or along a stream bank. Excellent examples of this type of erosion may be seen in the "bad-land" regions of North and South Dakota. In some regions ice is even more important than liquid water as an agent of erosion. This is true especially where there are glaciers. The ice mass of the glacier usually grinds up and removes all plants and plant parts as well as the upper layers of the substratum so that with the later retreat of the ice large areas of virgin soil or rock are laid bare. Sometimes when the water of a pond or lake freezes the expansion that takes place causes the ice to push against the shore and bring about erosion which results in bare areas. Wind is also an important agent of erosion, especially in regions of sandy soil where it may produce moving sand dunes or may dig out depressions in the sand known as "blow-outs." Gravity may produce a crumbling or slipping of land masses, bringing about land slides which result in bare areas.

Deposit is, in a sense, implied when we speak of erosion, since materials removed from one place must eventually be deposited somewhere else. However, as an agent for the production of bare areas, deposit is quite distinct from erosion. Running water may build flood plains, and sand bars may be built in a similar way by waves and tides. Wind, glaciers, and gravity are all agents of deposit since they must deposit the materials which they have moved by erosion. Volcanic dust is sometimes carried by the wind and deposited in such quantities that existing vegetation is buried and a bare area produced. Lava flows and other volcanic deposits form bare areas in the vicinity of their source.

The elevation or subsidence of a land mass, if great enough and rapid enough, will produce a bare area. There are also many climatic and biotic factors that may produce bare areas, though these are, for the most part, secondary rather than primary bare areas. For example, a drought may be severe enough to kill all vegetation on an area, a wind storm may destroy a forest, a snow slide may destroy the vegetation on a mountain side, a hail storm or a late frost may kill herbaceous plants, or lightning may start a fire which will destroy a forest (Fig. 93). Man is the most destructive of the biotic factors and destroys vegetation over the largest areas (Fig. 94). Other animals such as rodents, ants, or prairie dogs often destroy the plant life of small areas. Para-

Fig. 93.—A mountain side on which the forests have been largely destroyed by fire.

Fig. 94.—A forest of spruce and pine showing the destructive activity of man acting as a biotic factor.

sitic plants such as the dodder or a disease-producing fungus may become so abundant as to completely destroy the plants on a limited area.

Bare areas may be classified as sand, clay-gravel, rock, and water. Sand consists essentially of disintegrated rock. It is usually composed largely of grains of quartz and silicates but may have other minerals and even organic matter mixed with it. A clay-gravel substratum also consists of disintegrated rock. The soils classed under this head are extremely variable since they consist of varying proportions of sand, gravel and clay. Bare rock also varies greatly, both in hardness and in chemical composition. Water is of course always the same in chemical composition but it varies in the materials that are in solution in it and also in depth.

132. **The Causes of Succession.**—A sere must always begin on a bare area. Therefore, the causes of bare areas that have been discussed above may be considered the initial causes of succession. After the sere is once started there are various factors that cause it to continue. A change of climate in a region changes the climax vegetation and so brings about a succession of plant communities. Climatic changes are usually so slow, however, that, while they are valuable in the interpretation of the past history of vegetational changes, they are of little importance in the study of current seres.

On every part of the earth's surface that is not already level there is a tendency for the action of physiographic factors to result in a leveling of the land. This is brought about largely through erosion from the higher places and deposit in the depressions. These processes are influential in causing plant successions to continue.

By far the most important causes of succession, however, are biotic. Each plant community in a sere changes the environment in such a way that the habitat gradually becomes better suited to the component species of the immediately succeeding stage and less suited to the existing one.

The processes that are concerned in the biotic causes of succession may be grouped under three headings; namely, invasion, competition, and reaction. Invasion means the movement of plants from one area into another and their colonization in the latter. The movement from one area to another constitutes migration and the colonization of plants in a new home is known as ecesis. The various means by which plants migrate were discussed in Chapter XVI. Migration, however, must be followed by ecesis if the invasion of the new area is to be successfully completed.

Fig. 95.—*Coprinus comatus.* One of these mushrooms may produce more than 5 billion spores.

Most plants produce a great excess of disseminating bodies. A single pigweed (*Amaranthus retroflexus*) has been known to produce 2,350,000 seeds. A single specimen of the pasture mushroom (*Agaricus campestris*), according to an estimate based on results obtained with a counting apparatus, may produce 1,800,000,000 spores, while a large specimen of the shaggy mane mushroom (*Coprinus comatus*) (Fig. 95) may produce 5,240,000,000 spores. Some conception of this immense number may be obtained from the statement that, although these spores are microscopic in size, if the number from the above shaggy mane mushroom were placed end to end they would extend a distance of about 41 miles. But the world is full of plants now, so that, on the average, there is a chance for only one disseminule from each plant to grow. Thus, the great waste of seeds and spores through migration to unfavorable places is not a serious matter. The whole surface of the earth is bombarded with seeds and spores of innumerable kinds each year but after migration is completed ecesis can take place only under favorable conditions.

Although migration often proceeds over great distances the proximity of the young community to parent vegetation, or feeder vegetation as it may be called, is an important factor in controlling the rate at which invasion may proceed. As a rule the greater numbers of seeds and fruits fall within a few hundred feet of the parent plants so that the greater the distance of the feeder vegetation from the new area the less likely is migration to it to be attained. For this reason certain stages in the succession, those for which feeder vegetation is near by, are likely to develop much more rapidly than those that must be fed from a greater distance. Furthermore, the topography of the intervening area indirectly influences migration. High hills or a forest may act as barriers which more or less effectually prevent migration where it would take place quickly over a level, unbroken area.

Some of the more usual causes of the failure of ecesis are injury to the seeds during migration, over-crowding on the new area, competition with species already established, and migration to places that are ecologically unsuitable. If the seeds do not germinate, ecesis cannot be said to have started at all; if they produce seedlings but never reach maturity, ecesis is started but not completed; while, if the plants reach maturity and are able to carry on their reproductive function, ecesis may be said to have been completed and invasion to have taken place.

Competition, the second process involved in the biotic causes of succession, is a universal characteristic of plant communities. It occurs whenever two or more plants make demands in excess of the supply, increasing as the population increases until the community approaches the climax in maturity and then decreasing. It can exist, however, only between plants that are more or less equal in their demands. There is no competition in this sense between a parasite and its host, nor between a tree and an herb, but there may be competition between two trees or two herbs or between a tree seedling and an herb. Those species which compete in any way are called competitive species while those which can live in the same community without competing are called complementary species. In the younger stages of the succession competition is largely confined to the soil where the roots compete for water. As the population increases, however, competition may be as acute above the surface of the soil as below it. The competition that takes place in the air is largely for light.

In a forest there is an apparent root competition for moisture between the trees and the herbaceous vegetation and tree seedlings. Where the forest canopy is very dense there is often practically no undergrowth and this was formerly attributed to the inability of plants to grow in the dense shade. It has been found, however, in some places, that by digging a trench around a small area in such a forest in such a way as to cut off all roots entering the area an abundant undergrowth may develop, thus proving that lack of soil moisture is more important than lack of light in such a case. This, however, is somewhat different than competition between plants that make similar demands upon the environment. The trees, as the dominant plants, are in control and the undergrowth never has a chance to compete with them on anything like equal terms. Tolerance, or the ability of plants to grow under a forest canopy, is a complex phenomenon which is dependent upon several factors, the most important of which are probably the light and moisture relations. It is not, however, so much a question of competition as of enduring the conditions imposed by the dominant trees.

Reaction, the third biotic cause of succession, refers to the effects of the plants upon the habitat. These effects are quite variable in nature. As soon as the first plants appear on an area the soil-forming reactions begin. The weathering or disintegration of the rock, if the substratum is composed of rock, is hastened by the excretions from the plants and by the growth of roots in cracks and crevices. Wind-blown materials and water-borne detritus are caught by the plants and added to the soil. Dead plant bodies or parts of plants are also accumulated and become a part of the soil. The structure of the soil is also changed by the plants, in part by the same reactions that produce soil. The addition of humus, for example, decreases the average size of the soil particles and usually has a tendency to make the soil more mellow. Sometimes the addition of humus results in making the soil more compact. The precipitation of humus substances by the soil salts may even produce a "hard-pan" layer which is impervious to water and even to roots.

The reactions which affect the water content of the soil are extremely important. As a general rule, during the entire course of the succession the soil-water content is either increasing or decreasing. These effects are brought about indirectly through the building-up of soil, the increase in shade, etc. In the case of a xerarch succession the soil-water content increases while in a hydrarch succession it decreases so that in either case development is toward mesism. The nutrients that are in solution in the soil water are also modified by the reactions of the plants. They may be increased through the addition of humus by leaf fall or by other means or they may be decreased through the plants being eaten by animals or being removed from the land by man. The soil organisms, both parasites and saprophytes, are usually increased both in number of individuals and in number of kinds as the plant community develops.

17

The reactions above the surface of the soil usually increase the amount of shade and the relative humidity of the air and decrease the temperature and the wind velocity. The local climate is often actually changed by the development of climax vegetation, especially if the climax is a forest. This is brought about by the large amount of water that is tran-

Fig. 96.—A crustose lichen. (Photograph by Bruce Fink.)

spired by the plants. This increases the rainfall and results in a somewhat more humid climate. The number and kinds of aërial organisms are affected in ways quite comparable to those of the soil organisms.

The result of all these various reactions is that the vegetation is kept in a dynamic state and succession proceeds toward the climax. Vegetation is never entirely stable, but, since the climax association is the most mesic community that the climate will support, it cannot become any more mesic and, as compared to the earlier stages of the sere, it is relatively stable and will persist indefinitely unless there is a change of climate or the community is destroyed by one means or another.

Successions that are brought about by the reactions of the plants themselves are sometimes called autogenic successions while those caused by climatic or physiographic factors are called allogenic successions. It is probable that a succession is never entirely autogenic or entirely allogenic but it is frequently possible to recognize that a given case is largely the one or the other.

133. **Pioneer Stages of Succession.**—The environmental conditions on a bare area are extremely difficult for most plants. There is no protection from the light and heat of the sun during the day and nothing to check radiation at night. Also there is no protection from wind, and, therefore, evaporation is very rapid. Moisture conditions are extremely variable. After a rain there may be pools of water on rock or soil surfaces but these may dry up quickly and the substratum become very hot and dry. There is usually a complete lack of humus and many of the essential mineral salts may be lacking, or present in an unavailable form. The character of the surface is often such as to make it very difficult for plants to gain a foot-hold, either because of its hardness or its instability.

Due to these extremely severe conditions the pioneer plants in all xerarch successions are very xeric. On bare rock the first plants are lichens. Lichens are divided into three groups based on their growth-forms. These are crustose, foliose, and fruticose lichens. The crustose lichens (Fig. 96) are so-called because they form thin crusts on the surface of the substatum. They are the most xeric of all and are the first to appear on a rock surface. The foliose lichens (Fig. 97) are more or less leaf-like. They are as a rule somewhat less xeric and they follow the crustose forms along with some xeric mosses. The fruticose lichens (Fig. 98) are upright forms and usually appear later in the succession. On sand or clay-gravel the pioneer plants are ordinarily annual xeric herbs. The pioneer plants of a hydrarch succession are, of course, hydric, often floating or submerged, plants, but even here the conditions are much more severe than in later stages of the sere.

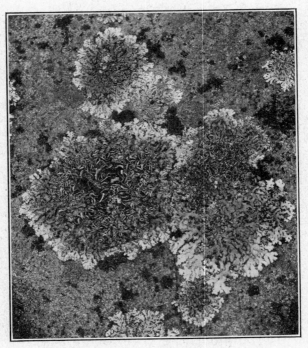

Fig. 97.—A foliose lichen. (Photograph by Bruce Fink.)

134. **Intermediate Stages of Succession.**—The intermediate stages include all of the stages between the pioneer community and the climax. In the pioneer community there are relatively few species and few individuals and the commu-

nity is, therefore, more or less open because the soil is not entirely occupied. The presence of the pioneer plants, however, by checking the wind velocity, producing shade, adding humus to the soil, etc., makes the habitat less extreme and prepares it for the invasion of other species. The

Fig. 98.—A fruticose lichen.   (Photograph by Bruce Fink.)

number of individuals increases from the pioneer stage to the climax and the community becomes less and less open. When the soil becomes fully occupied by plants the community is said to be closed. The number of species also increases until the climax is nearly reached and then it decreases.

The duration of the pioneer stages is relatively short and the duration of the intermediate stages increases until the climax stage is reached. This is relatively permanent.

The increase in population as the sere progresses is possible because the reactions of the plants are constantly making the habitat more mesic and less severe. The first plants following the pioneer species are likely to be herbaceous perennials. After the herbaceous plants have rather thoroughly occupied the soil, shrubs usually begin to appear

Fig. 99.—A young tree stage of a hydrarch succession. Willows and soft maples.

and there develop one or more definite shrub stages. This is likely to be true whether the sere is xerarch or hydrarch, though the kinds of shrubs will be different in the two cases. Trees may begin to come in at about the same time as the shrubs or soon after, and they increase in numbers until they become abundant enough to constitute a tree stage. In a xerarch succession the first trees may be conifers or they may be such xeric trees as the black and the white oaks (*Quercus velutina* and *Quercus alba*) and the hickories (*Carya ovata*, etc.). In a hydrarch succession the first trees are likely to be willows (*Salix*) and cotton wood (*Populus deltoides*) (Fig. 99). These first trees are followed by increasingly mesic species until the climax is finally reached.

135. **The Climax Stage of Succession.**—When the habitat becomes as mesic as is possible under the existing climatic and physiographic conditions the dominant species of the climax association appear and in time gain control of the environment. The climax association is the mature, adult organism of which the pioneer and intermediate communities are developmental stages. The climatic climax is the same throughout a climatic region whether it develops through a xerarch or a hydrarch succession. The course of development of a sere and its ultimate climax can usually be predicted, therefore, with perfect definiteness if the climax of the region is known.

The dominant species of the climax association exercise such a complete control over the environmental factors such as light, space, food materials, etc., that they prevent the entrance into the community of many other species of plants. For this reason, while the number of individuals in the climax community may be as great as in the intermediate stages, the number of species is ordinarily much smaller than in some of the earlier stages. The adjustment between the dominant species of a climax association and the environment approaches so near to perfection that the community is relatively stable and is likely to persist as long as the climatic and physiographic conditions remain unchanged.

136. **Factors Which Modify the Typical Succession.**—There are various topographic, physiographic, and biotic factors which modify the typical or ideal succession. Most often these factors affect only the rate; either accelerating or retarding the succession. In some cases, however, the succession is reversed temporarily so that its direction is away from, rather than toward, mesism, a phenomenon that is comparable with the cutting back of a small tree to a shrub stage. Such a shrub if left undisturbed under ordinary

conditions will develop again into a tree and in a comparable way the plant community which has been cut back by one means or another will, as a rule, develop again toward the mesic climax.

A topographic factor that influences the rate of development is the degree of slope. As a rule, the more nearly horizontal and level an area is the more rapid can the succes-

Fig. 100.—A shingle beach. Plant succession is very greatly retarded in such a place because of the unstable nature of the substratum and frequent flooding.

sion take place. With an increasing angle of slope the succession is more and more retarded and if the slope approaches too near the vertical no development can take place at all. The direction of slope is also of some importance in this respect. In a dry, hot region the vegetation of a north-facing slope will usually develop more rapidly than on a south-facing slope while in a cool, moist climate just the reverse is true.

An extremely important physiographic factor is erosion. This may either hasten or retard development or it may destroy vegetation and so put the sere back to a younger stage. Deposit is more likely to hasten than to retard a succession, though it may do either (Fig. 100).

Parasitic plants or animals may retard a succession by destroying certain kinds of plants or they may cut the sere back to an earlier stage, especially if they attack the dominant plants of the community. Grazing animals often produce similar effects. Man has, of course, caused very great modifications in successions over extensive areas, these changes being too numerous and far-reaching to be discussed here. Fire, which may be either a biotic or a climatic factor, is largely destructive though it may be only retarding in its effect.

REFERENCES.

Clements, Frederic E.: Plant Succession, Carnegie Inst. Washington Publ., 1916, **242**, 512.

Cooper, W. S.: The Climax Forest of Isle Royale, Lake Michigan, and its Development, Bot. Gaz., 1913, **55**, 1–44, 115–140, 189–235.

Cooper, W. S.: The Fundamentals of Vegetational Change, Ecology, 1926, **7**, 391–412.

Cowles, H. C.: The Causes of Vegetative Cycles, Bot. Gaz., 1911, **51**, 161–183.

Gleason, H. A.: Further Views on the Succession Concept, Ecology, 1927, **8**, 299–326.

Whitford, H. N.: The Genetic Development of the Forests of Northern Michigan, Bot. Gaz., 1901, **31**, 289–325.

CHAPTER XX.

PLANT SUCCESSION—Continued.

HAVING discussed plant succession in general in the preceding chapter we will describe in the present chapter some specific seres. Lack of space will not permit us to discuss the many different successions that are progressing in different parts of the world. We will therefore describe one typical sere for each of the four general types of bare areas, sand, clay-gravel, rock, and water, and make brief mention of only a few of the better known modifications.

137. Plant Succession on Sand.—Sand areas are found in North America along the shores of the Atlantic and Pacific Oceans, along the shore of Lake Michigan, in parts of the desert region of the southwest, in the sand-hill region of Nebraska, and in several other limited regions in the Mississippi Valley. We shall discuss the development of the beech-maple-hemlock association along the shore of Lake Michigan in Northern Indiana since this has been more thoroughly studied than any other sand succession.

An area of sand that is unoccupied by plants is exceedingly unstable. Sand which is thoroughly wet is not readily moved by the wind but after each rain the superficial layer quickly dries out and is then subject to being blown about by the wind. Any small object or an unevenness of the surface may serve as a slight check upon the wind and cause it to deposit the sand in a mound. This mound increases in size and becomes what is called a sand dune. Often the sand is more or less constantly being blown away from one side of such a dune and deposited on the opposite side so that the dune as a whole slowly moves with the wind and is spoken

(266)

of as an active dune. Such a dune, while very dry at the surface, usually contains an adequate amount of moisture a short distance beneath the surface. There is usually an almost total lack of organic matter and the essential mineral elements may also be practically lacking or present only in unavailable forms.

Fig. 101.—*Ammophila arenaria*, a sand pioneer, being replaced by *Arctostophylos uva-ursi* in the foreground and *Juniperus virginiana* in the background. (Photograph by A. G. Eldredge.)

Under these unfavorable conditions there are but few plants that can gain a foothold. In the xerarch succession the most successful pioneer is the beach grass (*Ammophila arenaria*) (Fig. 101). This grass and the wormwood (*Artemisia*) (Fig. 102) seem to be the only plants that can grow to full maturity in pure dune sand. They have extensive root systems which are composed of slender, much branched roots and they grow better in pure sand than where organic matter is present. Along with these are often found the sand-reed grass (*Calamovilfa longifolia*), the sea-rocket (*Cakile edentula*), the puccoon (*Lithospermum canescens*), sometimes the false heather (*Hudsonia tomentosa*), etc.

The hydrarch succession usually starts in a shallow depression. The pioneer is usually either the baltic rush (*Juncus balticus*) or the cottonwood tree seedlings (*Populus deltoides*). The cottonwood is especially efficient in enduring partial burial in sand. The trees keep on growing upward as fast as the sand piles up around them so that a cottonwood dune may be built up where there was originally a depression. Where the rush is the pioneer the filling of the depression

Fig. 102.—Wormwood (*Artemisia stelleriana*), a sand pioneer. (Photograph by A. G. Eldredge.)

is likely to take place more slowly. Gradually, however, hydric grasses, sedges, and mosses come in and with them, or following them, are such herbs as the water smart-weed (*Polygonum amphibium*), the marsh cinquefoil (*Potentilla pulustris*), etc., and later such shrubs as the sandbar willow (*Salix longifolia*) and the buttonbush (*Cephalanthus occidentalis*).

In the xerarch succession the soil is so unstable that although the *Ammophila* may check the movement somewhat it is not able to stabilize the dune entirely. It seems to grow best when sand is constantly being piled around it and as the dune advances the grass community moves with it, advancing in front and being torn out by the wind behind. The pioneer stage may be repeatedly formed and destroyed, therefore, and it is not until the dune gets far enough from the lake shore and the force of the wind is somewhat checked that the sand becomes less unstable, the pioneer plants die out, and the species of the intermediate stages begin to appear.

Some of the plants of the intermediate stages that appear rather early are the Solomon's seal (*Polygonatum commutatum* and *P. biflorum*), the bastard toadflax (*Comandra umbellata*), the bird-foot violet (*Viola pedata*), the dogbane (*Apocynum androsæmifolium*), the horse-mint (*Monarda punctata*), the blazing-star (*Liatris cylindracea* and *L. scariosa*), and some asters and goldenrods. Later some shrubs, woody lianas and trees begin to appear. The first trees are usually jack and white pines (*Pinus banksiana* and *P. strobus*). The herbaceous and shrub vegetation becomes abundant and is composed of a variety of species. Among the shrubs there are a number belonging to the heath family such as the bear-berry (*Arctostaphylos uva-ursi*), the shin leaf (*Pyrola elliptica*), and the aromatic wintergreen (*Gaultheria procumbens*).

Seedlings of oaks and other trees develop in this pine association and the next stage is a black oak association. The black oak is the dominant and sometimes almost the only tree. The evergreens disappear and are succeeded by such shrubs as the blueberry (*Vaccinium pennsylvanicum* and *V. vacillans*), various species of sumach (*Rhus*), the pin cherry and choke cherry (*Prunus pennsylvanica* and *P. virginiana*), sassafras (*Sassafras variifolium*), and the maple-leaved haw (*Viburnum acerifolium*). There are also many herbaceous plants such as goldenrod (*Solidago speciosa* and *S. hispida*), the milkweed and butterfly weed (*Asclepias syriaca* and *A. tuberosa*), the prickly pear (*Opuntia Rafinesquii*), and the false Solomon's seal (*Smilacina racemosa* and *S. stellata*).

The black oak association may persist for a rather long time but is gradually replaced by a more mesic oak association in which the red oak (*Quercus rubra*) is a prominent dominant. Finally the habitat reaches the highest degree of mesism, a thick layer of humus has formed over the sand, the water-holding capacity of the soil has greatly increased, the evaporation rate has decreased, and the climax forest, dominated by the beech (*Fagus grandifolia*) and the sugar maple (*Acer saccharum*), appears and persists indefinitely unless destroyed by one means or another.

138. **Successions on Clay or Clay-gravel.**—The clay-gravel successions that are best known are those that take place on glacial deposits. These have been studied in various places in the northeastern quarter of the United States and in southeastern Canada. The glacial deposits throughout these regions are very variable, some areas being almost pure clay and others consisting of more or less complex mixtures of clay, gravel and other materials. They are practically all occupied by plants at the present time so that opportunities for actually observing primary successions in the early stages are extremely rare. The best that are available for this purpose at present are the striplands of Illinois, Indiana and Ohio where the vegetation has been completely destroyed in the process of surface coal-mining.

As a result of stripping the soil is left as bare alternating ridges and furrows, the ridges varying from 3 or 4 feet to 30 or 40 or more feet in height (Fig. 103). In many cases these areas are left undisturbed for a long term of years and their revegetation takes place without any artificial interference. In Vermilion County, Illinois, these striplands are mostly on bottomland areas along streams. Here the pioneer plants are usually annual and perennial herbs. In the bottoms of the furrows the knotweeds (*Polygonum aviculare* and *P. persicaria*) are often the dominant and sometimes the only plants. In the more shallow furrows the barnyard grass (*Echinochloa crusgalli*) takes the place of the knot weeds or occurs along with them, and often scattered individuals of the giant ragweed (*Ambrosia trifida*) are present also. On the other hand, some of the deeper furrows, which lack adequate drainage, have water standing in them a greater part of the time. Here are found cat-tails (*Typha latifolia*) and occasionally water plantain (*Plantago*

Fig. 103.—Creating a bare area. Striplands, Vermilion County, Illinois.

alisma-aquatica). Just above the water there is usually a zone of cocklebur (*Xanthium commune*).

The ridges present somewhat more variety in their floras, although some of them are occupied almost exclusively by sweet clover (*Melilotus alba*) which grows 7 feet high and so thick that it is difficult to walk through. Other ridges are covered with such plants as wild aster (*Aster ericoides*), sunflowers (*Helianthus hirsutus* and *H. decapetalus*), ragweed (*Ambrosia artemisiifolia*), evening primrose (*Œnothera biennis*), black mustard (*Brassica nigra*), and prickly lettuce (*Lactuca scariola*).

The first woody plants are usually willow (*Salix nigra*)

and cottonwood, but this depends upon the proximity of communities from which these plants may migrate, and sometimes the buttonbush (*Cephalanthus occidentalis*) and the soft maple (*Acer saccharinum*), the white elm (*Ulmus americana*), the green ash (*Fraxinus lanceolata*), and the sycamore (*Platanus occidentalis*) come in almost as soon as the typically hydric pioneers (Fig. 104).   In any case they are sure to come sooner or later and are likely to be accom-

Fig. 104.—Mixed forest on striplands, Vermilion County, Illinois, twenty-five years after stripping.

panied by honey locust (*Gleditsia triacanthos*) and such lianas as wild grape (*Vitis cordifolia*) and poison ivy (*Rhus toxico-dendron*).   The elm, sycamore, and honey locust are commonly the dominant species of the edaphic climax forest of the bottomland in this region and such a forest may become well established on stripland in twenty-five to fifty years after stripping (Fig. 105).

A sere on an upland clay-gravel area would start in much the same way as the xerarch succession on striplands, the pioneer plants being xeric annual and perennial herbs.   These would be followed by a xeric shrub association dominated by such shrubs as the smooth sumach (*Rhus glabra*), the hazel (*Corylus americana*), and blackberries (*Rubus sp.*). The shrub stages would be followed by a xeric tree community in which the dominant species would be the black and the white oaks and the shagbark and the pignut hickories (*Carya ovata* and *C. cordiformis*).

FIG. 105.—Sycamore consociation on stripland, twenty-five years after stripping. The sycamore is an edaphic climax species.

In the tall grass prairie region, which includes a large part of Illinois and several states west of the Mississippi River, the dominant species of the climax association is the tall blue-stem grass (*Andropogon furcatus*). The xerarch succession here starts much the same as in the forest region, but the pioneer herbs are followed by the short blue-stem grass (*Andropogon scoparius*) and this in turn by the climax tall blue-stem association.

The hydrarch succession may be traced as it occurs in a slough. Here the bulrush (*Scirpus fluviatilis*) is at first the most abundant plant, though it may be accompanied

18

by many other kinds of water plants. The bulrushes begin to die as the slough becomes drier through filling and are replaced by sedges (*Carex sp.*) which dominate the second stage. The sedges are followed by slough grass (*Spartina Michauxiana*). Sometimes the slough grass follows the bulrush directly without an intervening sedge stage. The slough grass is followed by blue joint-grass (*Calamagrostis canadensis*) and tall panicum (*Panicum virgatum*), or by panicum alone, which, in turn, is finally replaced by tall blue-stem.

139. **Successions on Rock.**—Areas of bare rock are relatively infrequent and of limited extent. They are for the most part rocks that have been exposed through erosion by water or by glaciers. Rocks vary greatly in hardness and this factor is very important in determining the rapidity with which the earlier stages of plant succession may take place. Rocks are classified as igneous, sedimentary, and metamorphic. Igneous rocks are those which were melted and have solidified by cooling. They are glassy or crystalline in character and are usually very hard. Granite is a familiar example. Sedimentary rocks are those which have been laid down under water by mechanical, chemical, and biotic processes. They are composed of more or less rounded and worn fragments, are seldom crystalline, and frequently are quite soft. The common sandstones, limestones and shales are sedimentary rocks. Metamorphic rocks are those which have been changed from igneous or sedimentary rocks, usually by heat and pressure. They are usually harder than the rocks from which they are formed. Marble, for example, is metamorphosed limestone and slate is formed from shale.

An area of very hard rock affords no available water for plants except from dew and rain. Soft and porous rocks, however, contain varying amounts of water and this may be a factor of considerable importance. The presence or absence of cracks and crevices also are important in their influence on the rate of weathering and on the establishment of certain kinds of plants. The slope of rock surfaces may vary all the way from horizontal to vertical and this leads to great variations in exposure to climatic factors. A south-facing cliff is extremely xeric while a north-facing slope, because of its protection from heat and evaporation, may be almost mesic.

On a hard rock surface the first pioneer plants are crustose lichens of various species. They vary in color, some being pale green but others gray, black, yellow or red. Some are so thin that they appear like spots of paint on the rock. They grow very slowly and seldom cover the entire surface but they gradually disintegrate the rock superficially and produce a slight roughness which makes possible the growth of some xeric foliose lichens. These also grow very slowly but they hasten the disintegration of the rock somewhat and they catch some wind-blow dust and so start the building of a soil.

A very small amount of soil is enough to prepare the way for xeric mosses which will grow along with the lichens. As more soil accumulates xeric grasses and some other herbaceous seed plants appear. The species of seed plants that come in as pioneers depend upon the nature of the feeder vegetation, that is, the surrounding communities from which migrations may take place. They are likely to be such plants as golden-rod (*Solidago*), cinquefoil (*Potentilla*), chickweed (*Cerastium*), harebell (*Campanula americana*), etc. The accumulation of soil will now go on more rapidly and such xeric shrubs as blackberries (*Rubus*), smooth sumach (*Rhus glabra*), and sassafras (*Sassafras variifolium*) begin to appear. By this time the rock will be completely covered with soil containing a supply of humus, and trees gradually enter. The first trees are likely to be xeric oaks and hickories accompanied by various other species and these are followed in order by the climax mesic trees, hard maple and beech, accompanied by red oak (*Quercus rubra*), basswood (*Tilia americana*), etc. (Fig. 106).

The rock succession discussed above is outlined as it would normally occur on an area that was essentially horizontal. In the case of a vertical cliff the conditions are even more severe and succession is usually much retarded. The accu-

Fig. 106.—Remnant of a climax beech-maple forest. (Photograph by A. G. Eldredge.)

mulation of humus is impossible and the pioneer stage is likely to persist until physiographic changes have brought about more favorable conditions. This usually begins with a collection of soil at the base of the cliff. As this soil increases in amount the plants of later stages climb higher and higher and at the same time plants from the surrounding upland descend as the ledges near the top of the cliff become covered with soil. Eventually, of course, the whole rock surface will be covered with soil and plants, but this takes a very long time.

A rock canyon usually presents very complex and interesting ecological conditions. The head of a canyon is constantly eating its way back into the upland and so is always young, while farther down it is middle-aged, and at the mouth may be relatively mature. The pioneers in the young canyon are likely to be liverworts instead of lichens because of protection from the sun and the constant presence of moisture. Where the rocks are exposed to the sun, however, xeric lichens are the pioneers. In general, the succession is more or less comparable to that on a vertical rock cliff as the canyon broadens out and conditions become less severe. Successions in rock canyons have not been sufficiently studied to enable us to know accurately just what does happen. Such canyons, therefore, offer a fertile field for investigation.

140. **Successions in Water.**—Successions may take place either in standing water or in running water The successions in standing water have been more thoroughly studied than any others, due to the fact that often all stages can be found forming distinct zones around a single body of water.

In the normal succession in a depression that is not entirely unprovided with drainage, the pioneer plants are floating or submersed aquatics that grow in water 5 to 10 feet in depth. Characteristic plants are many kinds of algæ, the duckweeds (*Lemna*), the pond weeds (*Potamogeton*), etc. As the depression becomes filled and the water more shallow, 2 to 5 feet deep, plants of the second stage, which root at the bottom but have shoots which extend nearly to the top of the water, or float, in part, upon its surface, come in. This stage is characterized by water lilies (*Nymphea*) and such plants as the water crowfoot (*Ranunculus aquatilis*) and the water smartweed (*Polygonum amphibium*). In still shallower water, up to

2 feet, we find the bulrush-cat-tail stage characterized by such plants as the bulrush (*Scirpus*), the cat-tail (*Typha latifolia*), the pickerel weed (*Pontederia cordata*), the arrow leaf (*Sagittaria latifolia*), etc., whose shoots extend well above the water.

After the depression has filled to such an extent that the water table is just at the surface there appears a stage which is characterized by various species of sedges and grasses and such flowering herbs as wild iris (*Iris versicolor*), skull-cap (*Scutellaria*), water horehound (*Lycopus*), and several kinds of gentians (*Gentiana*). This stage is followed by the shrub stage in which the dominant plants are likely to be willows (*Salix*), alders (*Alnus*), button-bush (*Cephalanthus occidentalis*), and dogwoods (*Cornus*). The first trees to follow the shrubs are likely to be ashes, soft maples and elms. These are replaced later, as the substratum becomes drier, by the trees of the climax forest.

When the depression is poorly, or not at all, drained the normal aquatic succession is modified into a bog succession. In this the first three stages are like those of the normal succession but in the fourth stage a quaking bog is formed. This consists of a floating mat of vegetation which is held together by a network of roots and rhizoids of sedges and other plants and may extend out over the surface of the water for some distance. The mat appears like solid ground but walking upon it is like walking upon India rubber for it is depressed at each step and then springs up again so that one actually walks in several inches or more of water. Upon this floating mat are found many of the typical bog plants such as *Sphagnum* moss, cranberry (*Vaccinium*), the pitcher plant (*Sarracenia*), the sundew (*Drosera*), etc. As the mat becomes more stable and somewhat drier through the accumulation of dead organic matter the shrub stage appears. The first shrubs are usually the dwarf birch (*Betula pumila*), the leather-leaf (*Chamædaphne calyculata*), the bog rosemary (*Andromeda polifolia*), and the swamp blueberry (*Vaccinium corymbosum),* and they are followed later by such taller shrubs as the winterberry (*Ilex verticillata*) and the poison sumach (*Rhus vernix*). The first tree to appear on the bog is usually the tamarack (*Larix laricina*) which is followed later by spruces at the north, or deciduous trees at the south, and finally by the climax trees of the region.

The swiftly-running water of a young stream presents conditions that are unfavorable to most plants and the succession does not progress beyond two or three stages until the stream becomes more mature and the water more sluggish. Some of the plants that are found in the young stream are *Cladophora* and some other algæ, mosses of the genus *Fontinalis,* and some species of pondweeds and saxifrages. The later stages which finally take place in an old stream are very similar to the later stages in standing water.

REFERENCES.

Bray, William L.: History of Forest Development on an Undrained Sand Plain in the Adirondacks, New York State Coll. Forest. Tech. Publ., 1921, **13**, 47.

Cooper, W. S.: Plant Succession in the Mount Robson Region, British Columbia, Plant World, 1916, **19**, 211–238.

Cooper, W. S.: Vegetation Development Upon Alluvial Fans in the Vicinity of Palo Alto, California, Ecology, 1926, **7**, 1–30.

Croxton, W. C.: Revegetation of Illinois Coal Stripped Lands, Ecology, 1928, **9**, 155–175.

Ewing, J.: Plant Succession of the Brush Prairie in Northwestern Minnesota, Jour. Ecol., 1924, **12**, 238–266.

Forest, H. de.: The plant Ecology of the Rock River Woodlands of Ogle County, Illinois, Trans. Illinois State Acad. Sci., 1921, **14**, 152–193.

Gates, Frank C.: Plant Succession About Douglas Lake, Cheboygan County, Michigan, Bot. Gaz., 1926, **82**, 170–182.

McBride, J. F.: Vegetation Succession under Irrigation, Jour. Agr. Res., 1916, **6**, 741–760.

Pearsall, W. H.: The Development of Vegetation in the English Lakes, Considered in Relation to the General Evolution of Glacial Lakes and Rock Basins, Proc. Roy. Soc., London B., 1921, **92**, 259–284.

Robbins, W. W.: Successions of Vegetation in Boulder Park, Colorado, Bot. Gaz., 1918, **65**, 493–523.

Sampson, Arthur W.: Plant Succession in Relation to Range Management, U. S. Dept. Agr. Bull., 1919, **791**, 76.

Sears, Paul Bigelow: The Natural Vegetation of Ohio. III. Plant Succession, Ohio Jour. Sci., 1926, **26**, 213–231.

Taylor, Aravilla M.: Ecological Succession of Mosses, Bot. Gaz., 1920, **69**, 449–491.

Waterman, W. G.: Development of Plant Communities of a Sand Ridge Region in Michigan, Bot. Gaz., 1922, **74**, 1–31.

CHAPTER XXI.

PHENOLOGY.

PHENOLOGY, the word being a shortened form of phenomenology, is a branch of ecology that deals with the seasonal occurrence of the various vital phenomena of plants, such as leafing, blooming, fruiting, falling of leaves, etc. Interesting and valuable phenological studies can be made anywhere without expensive equipment and phenology thus lends itself well for field work for classes or for individual students of ecology. Such studies are very valuable in connection with work on plant communities since it is not possible to understand the morphology of an association, nor the relations of the component species to the environment, without knowing something of the phenology of the plants concerned. The time of flowering of any particular species of plants varies from year to year because of varying climatic conditions but there is sufficient regularity so that in periodic climates, such as are found throughout the United States, rather definite seasonal aspects can be recognized in most associations. Only three will be discussed in this chapter.

141. **Seasonal Succession in a Deciduous Forest.**—Considering a deciduous forest in the east-central United States at about 40° north latitude as an example, six seasons can be quite readily recognized. These are as follows:

A. *Winter Season.*—During the winter the trees are essentially inactive and have dropped their leaves as a means of conserving the water supply during a season when absorption is difficult or impossible. Most other plants are also in a resting condition either as rhizomes, corms, bulbs, tubers, wintergreen rosettes, or seeds. There are a few algæ and fungi, and perhaps a few mosses, that are more or less active all winter but in general the forest is in an inactive condition.

B. *Prevernal Season.*—The prevernal season begins with the first activity of the plants, usually late in March or early in April, and lasts until the leaves of the trees are out, usually in early May. Many trees bloom during this season as do also the early spring flowers. These early spring flowers, such as hepatica, bloodroot (*Sanguinaria canadensis*)

Fig. 107.—*Sanguinaria canadensis.* A prevernal flower.

(Fig. 107), spring beauty (*Claytonia virginica*), dutchman's breeches (*Dicentra cucularia*), etc., all take advantage of the short period when the forest is warm and sunny, before the trees have leaved. They are active only about three months and dormant during the remainder of the year. They are northern plants and perhaps are relics of the glacial period and have developed the three-month habit during that period.

The seedlings of many later blooming plants appear during the prevernal season.

C. *Vernal Season.*—The vernal season begins with the opening of the forest tree leaves and lasts until near the middle of June. This is the season of the later spring flowers, such as the Virginia cowslip (*Mertensia virginica*), the May apple (*Podophyllum peltatum*), the wild geranium (*Geranium maculatum*), the Solomon's seal (*Polygonatum biflorum*), the wild spikenard (*Smilicina racemosa*), the wild strawberry, (*Fragaria virginiana*), and many others. The most of these bloom during the month of May and by the first of June there begins to be a scarcity of wild flowers.

D. *The Æstival Season.*—The æstival season begins about the middle of June and lasts until about the middle of August. At the beginning of this season an entirely new crop of wild flowers appears, but they are found in open places along forest margins, in meadows, and along streams rather than in the shade of the forest. Many of the legumes, mints, figworts, roses, etc., bloom during this season (Fig. 108). The winter buds of the forest trees develop at this time.

E. *Serotinal Season.*—This season lasts from the middle of August until late in September and is characterized by the blooming of many tall coarse plants largely of the composite family. The harebell (*Campanula americana*) is also characteristic of this season. By this time forest tree activity has practically ceased above ground.

F. *Autumnal Season.*—The autumnal season usually begins late in September and extends to the beginning of winter in the middle or latter part of November. It is characterized by the blooming of such plants as the goldenrod and asters, and by the falling of leaves and the ripening of fruits.

142. **Seasonal Succession in a Desert Community.**—The desert vegetation in the vicinity of Tucson, Arizona, has been more carefully studied than has that of any other place in the world. Here four seasons are recognized and these will be discussed in the following paragraphs.

A. *Winter Wet Season.*—The secondary maximum of

precipitation for the year occurs in December and January and amounts to 2 or 3 inches of rainfall. The vegetation begins to awaken in January and a large number of plants

Fig. 108.—Prairie clover (*Petalostemum*), a flower of the æstival season. (Photograph by A. G. Eldredge.)

begin blooming early in February and mature their fruits in March and April when there is a decrease in the rainfall. The plants that bloom during the winter season may be classed into two groups, namely, winter perennials and

winter annuals. The factor which usually checks the awak-
ening of these plants in the early part of the winter is the
low night temperature which often is several degrees below
freezing. Sometimes, however, a few warm days in December will bring forth a crop of low annual herbs which may
almost reach the blooming stage only to be blighted by a
frost early in January. The most outstanding characteristic of these winter annuals which adapts them for desert
conditions is the remarkable power of resistance of the seeds.
These seeds are ripened and thrown onto the ground during
March and April. The surface layers of the soil reach temperatures above 100° F. during the summer months. The
summer rains soak both the soil and the seeds but still no
activity is shown. The summer cools into a rainless autumn
and finally the cooler nights are followed by the winter rains
of December and not until then do the seeds show signs of
life.

Many of the winter perennials lose their leaves with the
approach of the high temperatures of April and May and the
stems, bulbs, or root-stalks go into a resting condition from
which they do not awaken until the following December or
January, eight or nine months later, the entire period of
activity being limited to about one hundred days. Some,
however, such as the creosote bush (*Covillea tridentata*),
which has varnished leaves, and a few others with protective
coatings of cutin or hairs, retain their leaves during the greater
part of the year. No plants without protected surfaces
can do this because during the summer the relative humidity
is between 30 and 40 per cent and evaporation is, therefore,
very rapid.

B. *The Dry Fore-summer.*—The winter season may be
said to end about April 1st and is followed by the dry fore-
summer which comprises April, May, and June with a total
average precipitation of less than 1 inch and maximum
temperatures of 95° to 112° F. The evaporation exceeds the
precipitation in an enormous ratio but these severe conditions

bring into activity the spiny, succulent xerophytes. These succulents are of two general types; the one represented by the cacti with storage stems and the other by the yuccas and agaves with succulent leaves. Both of these types of plants bloom in great profusion during the dry foresummer.

C. *The Humid Mid-summer.*—This season begins about July 1st and extends nearly to the end of September. The temperature is exceedingly high but the greatest precipitation of the year is during July and August. Millions of seedlings spring up when the rains come and forty-eight hours may change the entire appearance of the landscape. Some perennials, such as the great barrel cactus, bloom at this time and there are many annuals among which are a number of spurges (*Euphorbia*) and several parasitic dodders (*Cuscuta*) which make a very rapid growth.

D. *The Dry After-summer.* — The dry after-summer extends through October and November which are rainless months. The grasses which started late in the humid mid-summer ripen their seeds and remain as dry tufts. Some other plants ripen their seeds during the early part of this season but in general there is an almost total cessation of vegetative activity.

143. **Phenology of the Pine-barren Region.**—Harshberger has studied the phenology of the pine-barren vegetation of New Jersey and the information here presented is taken from his book which is cited at the end of this chapter. His study included 548 pine-barren plants which is only 7 less than the total number of native species of the region.

The period of activity of the pine-barren vegetation extends through the seven months from the beginning of April to the end of October, leaving five months when the vegetation is practically dormant. There is very little activity in April, however, and in fact the active period for the majority of the plants, so far as flowering and fruiting is concerned, is in July, August and September, the culmination being reached in August. The opening of the leaves of the deciduous trees takes place largely in May and the leaves fall in October. The period of photosynthetic activity of the mature leaves is about four and a half months. The length of the flowering period varies greatly with different plants, from fifteen days for some trees, such as some of the willows and oaks, to one hundred and fifteen days for the forget-me-not (*Myosotis laxa*) and one hundred and thirty-five days for the water lily (*Nymphœa variegata*). Two hundred and sixty-three of the 548 species are in bloom during August although only 106 begin blooming in that month. Although the largest numbers of flowers are in bloom during the middle of the summer, the region is practically never without some plant in bloom from the middle of March to the end of October.

REFERENCES.

Harshberger, John W.: The Vegetation of the New Jersey Pine-barrens, XI, 329 p. Christopher Sower Company, Philadelphia, 1916.

Robertson, C.: Phenology of Entomophilous Flowers, Ecology, 1924, **5**, 393–407.

Wolfe, T. K.: Observations on the Blooming of Orchard Grass Flowers, Jour. Am. Soc. Agron., 1925, **17**, 605–618.

CHAPTER XXII.

THE DISTRIBUTION OF PLANT COMMUNITIES.

THE present and past distribution of plants over the surface of the earth and the causes thereof constitute the science of phytogeography or plant geography. This is a science that is closely related to plant ecology and it is, therefore, important that a student of ecology should know something of it. It is a large subject in itself, however, and space does not permit us to treat of it fully here. All that will be attempted in this chapter, therefore, is a brief and necessarily incomplete account of the present distribution of plant communities over the surface of the earth.

144. Deciduous Forest Communities.—The deciduous forests of the north temperate zone occur in regions where the annual rainfall is above 30 inches with more than one-half of it falling during the warm months. In the United States deciduous forest associations of varying floristic composition occupy nearly all of the area east of the Mississippi River and north of the Carolinas, Georgia, Alabama and Mississippi, except the northern part of Maine, parts of northern Michigan and the central part of Illinois. Parts of Missouri, Arkansas, Oklahoma, and Texas, and also southern Ontario, Canada, are occupied by similar forests (Fig. 109).

The greater part of central Europe was originally occupied by deciduous forests similar to those in the United States but containing a much smaller number of species. These original forests have been almost entirely cut off but reforestation has been extensively and successfully practiced in many places. In Asia deciduous forests occur, for the most part, in the eastern regions. They formerly occupied Eastern

(287)

Manchuria and Korea and extended northeastward in the Amur Valley as well as in Northern China and Japan.   In

Fig. 109.—A deciduous forest of yellow poplar and chestnut.   North Carolina. (Photograph by F. G. Plummer.   Courtesy of H. L. Shantz and the U. S. Department of Agriculture.)

the thickly populated parts, especially in China, the forests have been entirely removed so that it is necessary to go into the remote mountain districts to find typical forest associations. Some of these forests of Eastern Asia are as rich in species as any in the United States.

In tropical climates deciduous forests occur where the rainfall is from 45 to 90 inches or where there is a large annual rainfall but alternating wet and dry seasons resulting from the monsoon winds. The monsoon forests resemble rain forests during the wet season but most of the leaves are dropped during the dry season. These are found at their best along the southern and southeastern coasts of Asia. Where the rainfall is between 45 and 90 inches, which is insufficient to produce a rain forest, the communities are of the savannah type. This is a forest of somewhat xeric trees which are separated by park-like, grassy spaces. Such forests occupy nearly all of the central portion of Africa except the Guinea Coast and the Congo River valley. In South America savannah forests occupy most of the central portion east of the Andes Mountains with the exception of the river valleys and the sea coasts. A large portion of northwestern Australia is also occupied by savannah forests.

145. **Coniferous Forest Communities.**—Coniferous forests are found for the most part, where the seasonal distribution of the rain is similar to that in the deciduous forest region but where the annual precipitation and the temperatures are too low to support deciduous forests. An exception to this statement is found, however, in the southeastern part of the United States where the greater part of the coastal plain south of New Jersey and east of Texas, with the exception of the southern end of Florida, is occupied by coniferous forests although the rainfall is 50 inches or more throughout (Fig. 110). The limiting factors here are partly climatic and partly edaphic. The principal ones being the high evaporation rate and the sandy soil which is relatively infertile. The dominant trees in these forests are pines but there are also many cypress swamps along the Atlantic Coast and in the valley of the Mississippi River.

Elsewhere in the United States coniferous forests are

19

found in the greater part of Maine, the Green Mountains of Vermont, the Adirondack Mountains of New York (Fig. 111) and the highest parts of the Appalachian Mountains farther

Fig. 110.—Southeastern coniferous forest of long-leaf pine, loblolly pine, and short-leaf pine. (Photograph by E. Black. Courtesy of H. L. Shantz and the U. S. Department of Agriculture.)

south. They are also found in the northern portions of Michigan, Wisconsin and Minnesota, and throughout the mountainous portions of the western states (Fig. 112).

In Canada the northern boundary of the coniferous forests extends from the middle of the Labrador Coast westward across the middle of Hudson Bay and then north-westward

Fig. 111.—Mature spruce forest. Adirondack Mountains, New York. (Photograph by A. Gaskill. Courtesy of H. L. Shantz and the U. S. Department of Agriculture.)

to northern Alaska. Westward these forests extend to the foothills of the mountains. Southern Canada is practically all within this forest region with the exception of the southernmost parts of Ontario and portions of southern Alberta and

Saskatchewan. The mountains of western Canada, like those of the United States, for the most part support a belt of coniferous forests.

The only typical coniferous forests in continents other than North America are found in Northern Eurasia. There

Fig. 112.—Engleman spruce forest. Subalpine park in foreground. Uinta Mountains, Utah. (Photograph by Edward J. Ludkin. Courtesy of H. L. Shantz and the U. S. Department of Agriculture.)

they form a belt extending across Scandinavia, Russia and Siberia between the Arctic vegetation of the north and the deciduous forests farther south.

146. Broad Sclerophyll Communities.—Broad sclerophyll, or broad-leaved evergreen, communities are found in regions where the rainfall is rather low, usually about 20 inches, and more than one-half of it falls in winter when the temperature is least favorable for growth. The characteristic plants of these communities have broad evergreen leaves such as those of the holly and the live oak. The dominant plants are either trees or shrubs. Those communities in

Fig. 113.—*Adenostoma fasciculatum.* A common plant of the chaparral of Southern California. (Photograph by W. S. Cooper.)

which trees are dominant are called sclerophyllous forests while those in which shrubs are dominant are called chaparral. (Fig. 113).

In the United States broad sclerophyll communities are found most extensively in Southern California, extending southward into Lower California and northward along the mountains to Southern Oregon. The chaparral communities are more xeric and are most characteristic of the southern part of the range while the sclerophyllous forests occur more largely toward the north. Both types of communities are found, however, throughout the range.

Considerable areas of sclerophyllous vegetation are found in the Mediterranean region, especially on the north and east shores of the Mediterranean Sea and on the north coast of Africa between the Atlas Mountains and the Mediterranean. Both sclerophyllous forests and chaparral were originally found here at altitudes below 3000 feet but the forests have been almost entirely destroyed.

Broad sclerophyll communities are found in the southern part of Victoria, Australia, and in the extreme southern part of Western Australia. Some are also found in a limited area west of the Cape of Good Hope in South Africa. In South America similar communities are found on the west slope of the Andes Mountains in the central valley of Chile.

147. **Rain Forest Communities.**—Tropical rain forests are found in regions where the annual rainfall is from 90 to 150 or more inches, the relative humidity 70 to 100 per cent, and the temperature constantly high. The dominant plants in these forests are evergreen trees with broad, thin leaves. Some of the rain forests contain the densest, most luxuriant vegetation in the world. Often five distinct layers, three of which are tree layers, may be recognized. The first of these consists of trees 100 to 200 feet in height, the second of trees 50 to 100 feet in height, the third of trees 15 to 30 feet in height, the fourth of shrubs, and the fifth of herbaceous plants. There are great numbers of lianas which climb upon the trees or hang in great festoons from one tree to another, and the leaves of these contribute to the formation of a very dense forest canopy. Epiphytes are extremely numerous, the branches of the trees often being thickly covered with them. Those epiphytes that occur at the tops of the trees,

some of which are epiphylls, are very xeric but lower down they are progressively more mesic and near the ground there are epiphytic filmy ferns and other mesohydric species. The rain forest ordinarily does not present any brilliance of flowering plants because the flowers of the trees and lianas are high up where they are not easily seen and the shade is so dense that there are very few flowering plants on the forest floor although there are many pteridophytes and bryophytes.

The most luxuriant as well as the most extensive rain forests of the world are found in the valley of the Amazon River in South America. There are also some smaller areas on the north coast of South America, in Central America and Southern Mexico, and in the East Indies. Rain forests occur in Africa in the valley of the Congo River and along the coast of Guinea and the Liberian Gold Coast. They are also found on the east coast of Africa from the equator nearly to the Cape of Good Hope and also on the coast of the island of Madagascar. In Asia they occupy Indo-Malaysia from the southeastern slopes of the Himalaya Mountains to the Malay Peninsula, including most of this area, and also a large portion of both coasts of the peninsula of India. The northeast coast of Australia and most of the East Indian Islands have some areas occupied by tropical rain forests.

In the temperate zones there are some regions where the temperature and the rainfall are uniformly high that are occupied by forests that closely resemble the tropical rain-forests but are usually somewhat less luxuriant and somewhat different in floristic composition. These may be called temperate rain forests. They are found in parts of Mexico, in the southern end of Florida, in limited areas on the coast of Louisiana and Texas, and in Southern Japan. In South America they occur in Southern Chile and Patagonia. There are also limited areas in Australia and New Zealand adjacent to the tropical rain forests.

148. Grassland Communities.—Grasslands occur, for the most part, where the rain falls mostly during the summer and the total annual precipitation is not high. In North America the most extensive area of grassland occupies the most of the west central part of the United States between the Mississippi River and the foot hills of the Rocky Mountains except the southeastern part of Missouri, Arkansas, and the eastern part of Texas. There is also an eastern extension which includes most of the central and northern parts of Illinois and a northward extension which includes the southern portions of Alberta and Saskatchewan, Canada. There are also some smaller, more xeric grassland communities such as the Alpine meadows above timberline on the mountains, the mesquite grass associations in southern New Mexico and Arizona and the northern part of Mexico, and the bunch grass associations occupying much of the central valley of California.

The large central grassland area is about equally divided into eastern and western parts which are quite distinctly different. In the western part the rainfall, which is seldom over 22 inches annually, occurs primarily in the spring and early part of the summer. It seldom penetrates more than 2 feet into the soil and all of the available moisture is used up each year. Under such conditions the dominant species are low grasses and the communities are collectively spoken of as the short-grass plains vegetation (Fig. 114). In the eastern part, on the other hand, the rainfall is somewhat higher and the rainy season is longer. Here the rain-water penetrates to the water table and the total available water is seldom exhausted. Under these more favorable conditions tall grasses with deeply penetrating root systems are dominant and the communities are spoken of as tall-grass prairie vegetation.

Extensive areas of grassland, known as steppes, occur in Russia and Siberia and there is also an area of considerable extent in the eastern part of Australia. In Africa the central part of the southern end of the continent is occupied by grassland known as "veldt." In South America the most extensive grass communities are found in the central portions of Venezuela, Guiana and Brazil, and throughout the tropics where there are savannah forests the open spaces are occupied by grasslands.

Fig. 114.—Short-grass plains vegetation, Montana. (Photograph by H. L. Shantz. Courtesy of H. L. Shantz and the U. S. Department of Agriculture.)

149. **Desert Communities.**—Deserts are found where the annual rainfall is uniformly low, usually below 15 inches, and the evaporation rate is high. Because of these environmental conditions the vegetation is very xeric.

In the United States three general types of desert vegetation may be recognized. The first is the sagebrush (*Artemisia*) type which occupies the northern part of the desert region where the rainfall is fairly well distributed throughout

the year (Fig. 115).   This type of desert occurs extensively
in Wyoming, Western Colorado, Northern Arizona, Utah,
Nevada, Southern Idaho, Southeastern Oregon, Central
Washington, and smaller areas in the southern part of
British Columbia, Canada.   Cacti are largely absent from
this type of desert.   The southern part of the desert region
is occupied largely by the creosote bush (*Covillea tridentata*)

Fig. 115.—Sagebrush desert.   Utah.   (Photograph by H. L. Shantz.
Courtesy of H. L. Shantz and the U. S. Department of Agriculture.)

and cactus desert.   The climate is characterized by two
rainy seasons, one in winter and one in summer, and by high
temperatures and high evaporation rates.   This type of
desert is found in Southern Nevada, Southern California,
Southern and Western Arizona, Southern New Mexico, and
Western Texas, and extends southward into Mexico.   The
third type of desert, which occupies undrained depressions,
is the salt desert.   It is characterized by the greasewood
(*Sarcobatus vermiculatus*), the pickleweed (*Allenrolfea occi-*

dentalis), the saltgrass (*Distichlis spicata*), etc. The plants are, therefore, halophytes. The largest area of this type is the Great Salt Lake Desert, West of Great Salt Lake in Utah. Smaller areas are found throughout the desert region but especially in Nevada.

In South America the desert communities occupy a narrow strip west of the Andes Mountains from Peru to Northern Chile. They have a cactus type of vegetation with many mesquite (*Prosopis*) and *Acacia* shrubs. Nearly one-half of the continent of Australia is occupied by deserts. They are found in the central and west central parts and their vegetation consists largely of bunch grasses and *Acacia* and *Casuarina* shrubs. The Sahara Desert of North Africa is the most famous desert in the world as well as one of the most extensive. The greater part of this desert is quite rocky while about 10 per cent of the total area is sandy. Some of the sandy portions are characterized by active dunes and an almost total absence of vegetation, and the vegetation elsewhere is rather scanty except during the rainy season which occurs in late winter and early spring and is characterized by an abundance of annual plants. There is a smaller desert region in South Africa north of Cape Colony. The extensive desert region of Asia, which stretches across Arabia and Mesopotamia and ends in the Desert of Gobi in central Asia, is in reality a continuation of the Sahara Desert of Africa and the vegetation is similar except that there are larger proportions of sandy and saline deserts than in Africa. In the Gobi Desert there is an abundance of tulips during the rainy season.

150. **Arctic Communities.**—The Arctic region includes all of the territory north of the tree line, a line which is rather close to the July isotherm of 10° C. The environmental conditions are unique and severe. The subsoil is perpetually frozen. The growing season is but little more than two months long, beginning in June and ending in August, but during this time light is continuous or nearly so. Under such conditions the plants are very dwarf and very xeric.

The total vegetation, which is entirely treeless, may be called tundra, although it varies greatly from place to place. Most of the species are wide-spread, many of them being circumboreal and also extending far to the south on mountains.

In North America the southern boundary of the Arctic region extends from Labrador westward across the middle of Hudson's Bay and then northwestward and across the northern part of Alaska. However, tongues of the subarctic forests extend many miles beyond this boundary along streams at various places. The drier parts of the tundra are occupied largely by grass associations except that the boulders and other rocky places are covered with mosses and lichens. Along with the grasses are many dwarf shrubs and perennial herbs. Most of the herbs have either the rosette habit or the cushion habit. In the wetter parts of the tundra many *Sphagnum* bogs occur, the *Sphagnum* moss being accompanied by various other plants that are characteristic of the bogs farther south. The northernmost parts of the region are occupied largely by rock tundra in which the vegetation is composed almost entirely of lichens and mosses with a few grasses and other seed plants. The "reindeer moss," which consists of one or more species of lichens, is especially characteristic of the North American tundra. It may grow a foot high and thickly cover extensive areas, being interrupted only by the paths of reindeer. The vegetation of Northern Siberia is very similar to that of Arctic America except that moss tundra, in which the dominant plants are species of *Polytrichum*, is more characteristic of Siberia.

Among the characteristic herbaceous flowering plants of the Arctic region are many that belong to the same genera that are familiar farther south, such as buttercups, chickweeds, anemones, saxifrages, primroses, crucifers, cinquefoils, several composites, and the Arctic poppy. Among the woody plants are dwarf willows and birches and such members of the heath family as *Rhododendron, Cassiope, Arctostaphylos*, and *Vaccinium*. The only conifer is a dwarf juniper.

151. **Alpine Communities.**—Alpine vegetation is found near the tops of the higher mountains all over the world. In going up the side of a high mountain one encounters varia-

Fig. 116.—*Pinus flexilis* at timber line on Long's Peak, Colorado. (Photograph by Raymond J. Pool.)

tions in climate comparable to those encountered in going north or south from the equator and these variations in climate lead to a recognition of more or less definite belts of vegetation. Usually four of these belts or zones of vegetation can be recognized, the lowermost being called basal, the second montane, the third subalpine, and the fourth, or uppermost, alpine. The basal zone consists of vegetation that is similar to that of the adjacent plain or valley. The montane zone is usually more luxuriant than the basal and ordinarily consists of forest communities, either deciduous or coniferous. The subalpine zone is more xeric. It consists largely of coniferous forest, but the trees are dwarf and at timber line form the characteristic "elfin timber" (Fig. 116). There are also frequent open spaces which are occupied by grasses and flowering plants. Above the tree line is found the true Alpine meadow which becomes more and more dwarf as it ascends the mountain. The brilliance and profusion of bloom encountered in the Alpine meadows cannot be matched anywhere else. If the mountain is not too high the Alpine meadow may cover the top but the highest mountains are covered by perpetual snow and so are destitute of vegetation while some others have only lichens and a few xeric mosses at their summits.

REFERENCES.

Bews, J. W.: Some General Principles of Plant Distribution as Illustrated by South African Flora, Ann. Bot., 1921, **35**, 1–36.

Campbell, Douglas Houghton: An Outline of Plant Geography, The Macmillan Company, New York, 1926, ix, 392.

Cannon, William Austin: Plant Habits and Habitats in the Arid Portion of South Australia, Carnegie Inst. Washington Publ., 1921, **308**, VIII + 139, 32 pl. 31 fig.

Fairchild, David: The Jungles of Panama, Nation. Geog. Mag., 1922, **41**, 131–146, 14 fig.

Hill, Albert F.: The Vegetation of the Penobscot Bay Region, Maine, Proc. Portland (Maine) Soc. Nat. Hist., 1923, **3**, 305–438, fig. 1–50.

Holttum, R. E.: The Vegetation of West Greenland, Jour. Ecology, 1922, **10**, 87–108, pl. 3–5.

Kenoyer, L. A.: Plant Life of British India, Sci. Monthly, 1924, **18**, 46–65.

MacCaughey, Vaughan: Vegetation of the Hawaiian Lava Flows, Bot. Gaz., 1917, **64**, 386–420.

Ridley, H. N.: The Distribution of Plants, Ann. Bot., 1923, **37**, 1–30.

Salisbury, E. J.: The Geographical Distribution of Plants in Relation to Climatic Factors, Geograph. Jour., 1926, **67**, 312–342.

Shantz, H. L.: The Natural Vegetation of the Great Plains Region (U. S. A.), Ann. Assn. Am. Geog., 1923, **13**, 81–107, pl. 3–8, 2 fig.

Shantz, H. L. and Zon, Raphael: The Natural Vegetation of the United States, U. S. Dept. Agric. Bur. Agric. Econ. Atlas of American Agriculture, Pt. 1; Sect. E., 1924, 29 p., 60 fig., 3 maps.

Waller, A. E.: Crop Centers of the United States, Jour. Am. Soc. Agron., 1918, **10**, 49–83.

Wells, B. W.: Major Plant Communities of North Carolina, Agric. Exp. Sta. Tech. Bull., 1924, **25**, 3–20. 14 fig.

Whitbeck, R. H.: Economic Geography of South America, McGraw-Hill Book Company, New York, 1926, p. 430.

CHAPTER XXIII.

APPLIED ECOLOGY.

PLANT ecology is the most intensely practical of the plant sciences. It deals with the interrelations between plants and their environments and since man is an important part of the environment of plants, therefore, ecology includes all the interrelations between man and plants and hence all of applied botany. If, therefore, we were to take ecology out of botany or any of its subdivisions there would be nothing left that would have any application to the affairs of man. For this reason it is essential that anyone preparing to pursue any branch of economic biology be trained in ecology.

Obviously it would require volumes to deal in a comprehensive way with the entire field of applied ecology. In this chapter, therefore, we shall discuss briefly some of the most common applications, primarily for the purpose of making clear the fact that ecology is a practical science.

152. **Forest Ecology.**—Forestry, wherever it is successfully practised, is based entirely upon ecological principles. Practical foresters are realizing this more and more and are coming to recognize the need of training in plant ecology for anyone who is preparing for any phase of forestry as a life work. The forester should be perfectly familiar with the life cycles and the phenology of the trees under his care. He should understand such physiological processes as respiration, absorption, and transpiration and should know how these and other activities of the plant are affected by such environmental factors as heat, light, moisture, soil variations, etc. It is necessary also that he understand the methods of reproduction of each species, whether by seeds or by vegetative

shoots, and the most favorable conditions for reproduction. He should know what species of trees are ecologically suited to the conditions in his forest, both of native and foreign species, and whether they will grow best in pure stands or in mixed stands. The purpose for which trees are grown, whether for lumber, fence posts, railroad ties, etc., or whether they are being grown as a windbreak or to prevent erosion, influences the choice of species and makes it necessary to understand the characteristics and habits of growth of the various kinds. In order to properly care for and protect the forest it is necessary that the forester understand the dangers from tree diseases, insects, fire, and storms, and the effects of over-grazing and over-cutting. Extremely important also, of course, is a knowledge of dominance and of plant succession in relation to natural reproduction in the forest.

Much of the information that is so essential to a forester can at present be taught in courses in plant ecology and in technical forestry. There is a very large number of pressing problems in forest ecology, however, that are awaiting solution and there is urgent need for an increased number of trained workers in this line of research.

153. **Grazing Problems.**—Millions of acres of grazing lands in the western part of the United States have been injured to a greater or less degree by over-grazing so that the number of head of stock that might otherwise be pastured on them is materially decreased. Until ecological methods were applied there was no reliable means of recognizing over-grazing in its early stages. The usual method of estimating the condition of the range was based on observations on the general abundance and luxuriance of the forage supply and the condition of the stock being grazed. These general observations do not enable one to recognize over-grazing until large numbers of the most valuable plants have been destroyed.

By applying the principles of plant succession to the

problem of over-grazing it is possible to overcome many of the difficulties. Taking the ranges in central Utah as an example four major plant associations are recognized. In the order of their position in the successional series these are the ruderal weed association, the foxglove-sweet sage-yarrow association, the porcupine grass-yellow brush association, and the wheat-grass association. The wheat-grass association is the most permanent and will endure over-grazing longer than any other type and it makes very efficient pasture for cattle and horses but is not quite so good for sheep. The porcupine grass-yellow brush association contains a larger number of palatable species and will probably support more stock than any other type. The other two associations are due to excessive over-grazing and do not furnish valuable pasturage.

Any area on this range which is ungrazed or only moderately grazed develops eventually into the wheat-grass association while more intense grazing causes the wheat-grass to be replaced by the porcupine grass-yellow brush association and excessive over-grazing brings about the appearance of the earlier stages of the succession. Since the porcupine grass-yellow brush association is the most valuable of all, the most successful scheme of management is to graze just heavily enough to prevent the development of wheat-grass but not heavily enough to destroy the porcupine grass-yellow brush association. Thus by staking out permanent areas on the range and making observations from time to time for the appearance of species belonging to the preceding or following stages of the succession it is possible to increase or decrease the number of head of stock grazed before any appreciable damage has been done.

154. **Indicator Vegetation.**—We have shown in the preceding paragraph how plants characteristic of certain stages of a sere may be used as indicators of grazing conditions. There are many other practical uses that may be made of native plants as indicators of present conditions and often

20

of past or future conditions as well. Every plant is a measure of the conditions under which it grows and therefore it indicates how other plants may behave in the same habitat. The only thing that limits our use of native plants as indicators of environmental conditions is our lack of accurate knowledge concerning so many of the ecological relations of plants.

Either single plants or plant communities may be used as indicators, the communities being somewhat more significant than single plants or single species. The most important species in the community are the dominants and they may indicate past and future as well as present conditions. The native communities may be used to indicate the kind of practice that will prove most successful, that is, whether agriculture, grazing, or forestry should be practiced. They may indicate whether ordinary humid farming, dry farming, or irrigation farming should be used. For example, a tall-grass association indicates humid farming conditions while a short-grass association indicates dry farming and a sage-brush association indicates irrigation farming. Even the kinds of crops that are best suited to a region may be indicated by the native vegetation. Thus the areas of maximum production of corn and of winter wheat correspond to areas where the native grass associations are dominated by species of *Andropogon* while spring wheat and durum wheat reach their best development where *Stipa spartea* and *Agropyrum glaucum* are dominant. It is undoubtedly true that a land classification based on a thorough study of the indicator value of the native vegetation would be much more valuable than a classification made on any other basis.

155. **Crop Production.**—The entire problem of crop production is an ecological problem since it is concerned solely with the relation of crop plants to the environment. Before planting the seeds of a crop plant it is necessary to select a place that is ecologically suitable in its climatic and edaphic factors, and to prepare the seed-bed in the way demanded

by the ecological adaptations of the plant concerned. After the seeds have germinated it is necessary to know what methods of cultivation will make the habitat most favorable for development of the plant. The problems of soil fertility are ecological problems. Crop rotations are based upon the ecological relations of the crop plants concerned. Thus it is readily seen that the art or vocation of crop production is solely applied ecology. Crop ecology is, therefore, an all-important part of agronomy and is based, of course, upon general plant ecology.

156. Symbiotic Phenomena.—The practical applications of studies in symbiosis are many and varied. We have already pointed out some of the applications of studies of plant communities, which represent social disjunctive symbiosis, and the grazing problems that we have discussed fall under antagonistic nutritive disjunctive symbiosis. Pollination studies are extremely important from an economic point of view. The business of honey production is based entirely, of course, upon the symbiotic relation between bees and flowers. The commercial production of figs in America was entirely impossible until the symbiotic relation of the fig tree to a pollinating insect had been studied. The successful production of vegetables and fruits in greenhouses has depended in some cases upon pollination studies. The symbiotic relations between crop and ornamental plants and disease-producing organisms are, of course, of vast importance to man. In fact the science of plant pathology deals almost solely with symbiotic phenomena. The symbiotic relation between legume plants and nitrogen-fixing bacteria can scarcely be over-estimated. The successful cultivation and propagation of orchids depends upon a knowledge of their symbiotic relation with endotrophic mycorhizal fungi, and this is more or less true also of the cultivation of blueberries and other members of the heath family such as *Rhododendrons* and mountain laurel (*Kalmia*). The exact relationship between ectotrophic mycorhizal fungi and their host plants, especially in the case of forest trees, is still a somewhat unsettled question and much work must yet be done before these symbiotic structures will be fully understood. It is urgently important to the practice of forestry to know whether these mycorhizas are of vital importance to forest trees or not.

157. Landscape Gardening.—Ecology is as fundamental to landscape gardening as to forestry and crop production. It is as essential for the landscape gardener as for anyone else concerned with the growing of plants to know the general ecological relations of each species of plants with which he deals. Furthermore, it is essential that he have a thorough training in the structure and development of plant communities in order that he may make naturalistic plantings intelligently. He should understand the significance of ecological equivalents in order that he may vary the floristic composition of his plantings without sacrificing the optimum habitat conditions for the plants. The symbiotic relations between ornamental plants when planted in groups or in extensive communities is a field about which we know surprisingly little. It is well known that plants do influence one another, that some species get along well in the same planting and others do not, but these facts have never been organized or classified and the reasons for them are very obscure. This is, therefore, another very fertile field for future investigation. This is especially true of symbiotic relations below the surface of the soil, that is, the interrelations of the root systems of ornamental plants.

REFERENCES.

Baker, O. E.: The Agriculture of the Great Plains Region, Ann. Assn. Am. Geog., 1923, **13**, 109–167.

Boerker, R. H.: A Historical Study of Forest Ecology—Its Development in the Field ofBotany and Forestry, Forestry Quarterly, 1916, 1–53.

Boerker, R. H.: Some Fundamental Considerations in the Prosecution of Silvicultural Research, Jour. Forestry, 1918, **16**, 792–806. 871–887.

Bruner, W. E. and Weaver, J. E.: Size and Structure of Leaves of Cereals in Relation to Climate. A Study in Crop Ecology, Univ. Studies Univ. Nebraska, 1923, **23**, 163–200, 7 fig.

Burgess, Paul S.: The Yield and Mineral Content of Crop Plants as Influenced by Those Preceding, Rhode Island Agric. Exp. Sta. Bull., 1924, **198**, 1–25.

Burgess, Paul S. and Pember, F. R.: Active Aluminum as a Factor Detrimental to Crop Production in Many Acid Soils, Rhode Island Agric. Exp. Sta. Bull., 1923, **194**, 1–40, 6 fig.

Clements, Frederic E.: Plant Indicators. The Relation of Plant Communities to Process and Practice, Carnegie Inst. Washington Publ., 1920, No. 290, XVI. 388 p. 92 pl.

Lutz, Harold J.: Trends and Silvicultural Significance of Upland Forest Successions in Southern New England, Yale University School of Forestry Bull., 1928, **22**, 1–68.

Lynn, J. C. and Lynn, D. Anderson: Observations on the Improvement of Poor Pasture in the West Riding of Yorkshire, Ann. Appl. Biol., 1924, **11**, 135–152.

Roberts, Edith A. and Rehmann, Elsa: American Plants for American Gardens, The Macmillan Company, New York, 1929, p. 131.

Sampson, Arthur W.: Plant Succession in Relation to Range Management, U. S. Dept. Agric. Bull., 1919, **791**, 76 p., 26 fig.

Sarvis, J. T.: Effects of Different Systems and Intensities of Grazing upon the Native Vegetation at the Northern Great Plains Field Station, U. S. Dept. Agric. Bull., 1923, **1170**, 1–45, 9 pl., 11 fig.

Smith, J. Warren: Agricultural Meteorology. The Effect of Weather on Crops, 1920, XXII + 304 p., 8 pl., 88 fig., Macmillan Company, New York.

Toumey, James W.: Foundations of Silviculture Upon an Ecological Basis, John Wiley and Sons, New York, 1928, **25**, 438.

Waller, Adolph E.: Crop Centers of the United States, Jour. Am. Soc. Agron., 1918, **10**, 49–83.

Waller, Adolph E.: The Relation of Plant Succession to Crop Production, Ohio State Univ. Bull., 1921, **25**, 7–74, 15 fig.

Weaver, J. E.: Root Development of Field Crops, McGraw-Hill Book Company, New York, 1926, 290 p., 115 fig.

Weaver, J. E.: Plant Production as a Measure of Environment. A Study in Crop Ecology, Jour. Ecol., 1924, **12**, 205–237, pl. 1–5, 14 fig.

APPENDIX.

(FOR THE TEACHER.)

SUGGESTIONS CONCERNING LABORATORY AND FIELD WORK.

NEARLY every teacher of any branch of biology finds it necessary to work out his laboratory and field exercises for the reason that it is impossible for anyone to make a manual, or set of exercises, that will fit all localities and all working conditions. It is believed, however, that the following suggestions will prove helpful as a working basis, especially for teachers who are offering a course in plant ecology for the first time or who are unfamiliar with methods of carrying on field work. They are intended only as suggestions and should be modified to meet the varying needs of individual classes of students.

The Scientific Method.—Every course in any science should have as one of its chief aims the teaching of the inductive method which is the method of science. In the practical use of this method one first accumulates as many data as possible on the questions involved. He then classifies and evaluates the data and frames hypotheses to explain them. Finally he compares these hypotheses with known facts in every possible way and draws definite conclusions as to the truth or falsity of each. To train students in this orderly method of thinking is the greatest and most valuable thing that any teacher can do. It is true that the students must be expected to acquire a certain amount of information, but

(311)

the mere acquisition of information is the easiest part of scientific training. The information can practically all be found in books and the simplest and quickest way to get it is to go to the books for it. In the laboratory and field work the chief concern of both teacher and student should be with mental development; with growth in ability to acquire data and to make use of these data in arriving at conclusions through scientific thinking. This mental growth is more likely than anything else to lead the students to an enthusiastic love of the subject being pursued for nearly everyone gets pleasure from doing things that lead to personal accomplishment and that is what the scientific method enables us to do. The problem method is the accepted method for teaching scientific thinking and certain problems will be suggested in some of the following paragraphs.

Laboratory versus Field Work.—Plant ecology is pre-eminently a field subject. Most phases of it can be studied successfully only in the field. Students of ecology should, therefore, spend just as much time as possible in the field where the plants are at home. There are some phases of ecology, however, such as ecological anatomy, that can best be studied in the laboratory and this should be done when the weather is too inclement for field work. Except during the severest part of the winter the weather is seldom so inclement that field work cannot be done. It is good practice to tell students at the beginning of the course that all field trips will be taken as planned regardless of the weather. This is the only way to avoid complaints and absences on account of the weather for the weather is seldom exactly right and if one waits to take his field trips on days when the climatic conditions are satisfactory to everyone he is not likely to do much field work.

Field Work in Winter.—No great amount of work can be accomplished on a field trip unless the students are reasonably comfortable, but if they can be induced to dress in such a way as to remain comfortable much profitable field work can be done during the winter months. Most students are surprised to find that there are many plants in addition to evergreen trees that remain green all winter and one or more trips may be made to find rosette plants and others that are "winter greens." A good trip can be planned for the study of the growth habits of stems, especially if a visit to a greenhouse may be included. The greenhouse will also offer opportunity for studying variations in size, form, and arrangement of leaves. Profitable trips may also be made, out of doors, to study the resting condition of various kinds of plants with special reference to protection against loss of water, and to study such symbiotic phenomena as are evident in winter.

SUGGESTED PROBLEMS.

1. To discover what plants remain green during the winter season.

2. To discover whether "winter greens" are more abundant on uplands or on lowlands.

3. To find how many variations in stem habits there are on the campus and in the greenhouses.

4. To find how many variations in size, shape, and arrangement of leaves there are in the greenhouses and to explain their ecological significance.

5. To discover how many symbiotic phenomena are in evidence in a wood-lot during winter.

Ecological Anatomy.—Studies in ecological anatomy must be carried on largely in the laboratory. Since leaves are much more plastic than roots and stems more time is devoted to them. The few problems stated below will serve to suggest others.

SUGGESTED PROBLEMS.

1. To make a comparison between the stem and root of a mesic plant as to internal structure, and to explain the ecological significance of the differences.

2. To make a comparison between a rhizome and a root as to internal structure.

3. To discover which of the leaves provided is mesic, which xeric, and which hydric. (Students should cut their own sections if possible, but if time or facilities do not permit this, prepared slides may be used.)

4. To discover which of the leaves provided is a sun leaf and which a shade leaf. (Sun and shade leaves of hard maple make good material for this.)

5. To classify each of the leaves studied as diphotophyll, diplophyll, staurophyll, or spongophyll.

Symbiotic Phenomena.—The studies that may be made of symbiotic phenomena are almost unlimited. It is well to advise students to be on the look-out for symbiotic relations on all field trips made in addition to making some trips especially for these studies. Numerous structures resulting from symbiosis make good material for laboratory work.

Suggested Problems.

1. To discover how a dodder plant obtains food from its host.

2. To discover what kinds of trees in a wood-lot have ectotrophic mycorhizas.

3. To compare the mycorhizas of a hickory tree with those of an orchid.

4. To make a list of the lianas in a wood-lot and discover which ones twine in a clockwise and which in a counterclockwise direction.

5. To investigate the internal structure of a lichen.

6. To discover how certain kinds of flowers are pollinated.

7. To find as many kinds of insect galls as possible.

Instrumental Methods.—It is not essential that a beginning class in ecology be provided with expensive equipment. The use of instruments for the measurement of physical factors is so important, however, that, if they can be provided, students should have an opportunity to do at least some work with them, and in almost every case at least some instruments can be provided. In order to obtain accurate and valuable data on most of the physical factors it is necessary to take long series of measurements. This is usually impossible for a beginning class. Two methods have been

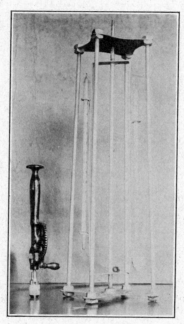

Fig. 117.—A cog psychrometer.

used with classes at the University of Illinois for teaching the use of instruments and the significance of instrumental measurements. By one of these methods five diverse habitats were selected and the class was divided into five groups, one for each habitat. Each group was provided with a photometer for taking light readings, an anemometer for measuring wind velocity, a psychrometer for measuring relative humidity (Fig. 117), a stop-watch, a soil thermometer, and a soil can for taking a sample for determination of soil-water content. Each group worked upon a time-schedule previously agreed upon so that each kind of measurement was made simultaneously in all five habitats. The groups then exchanged data and were asked to explain the differences in vegetation in the five habitats on the basis of the differences in physical factors. The second method used was similar to the first except that instead of working on a time-schedule each group of students was given a set of instruments and told to devise methods of making a thorough investigation of one of the five habitats. While this method gave less accurate data than the former it had the advantage of placing the students more upon their own responsibilities with fewer specific directions to follow.

Suggested Problems.

1. To learn to use common instruments for making measurements of the physical factors of the environment.

2. To make a thorough investigation of the physical environment of a single plant.

3. To make a comparison of five habitats as to the physical factors of the environment.

4. To discover reasons for differences in vegetation in five habitats.

5. To compare the evaporation rates in five habitats. (Porous clay-cup atmometers would be useful for this) (Fig. 118).

Quadrat Methods.—A quadrat is a square area used for making studies of vegetation (Fig. 119). A quadrat may be of any convenient size such as 1 meter square or 10 feet square or 100 feet square. Quadrats are used in various ways and are designated accordingly. A list quadrat is one in which the plants are counted and a list is made of the species with the number of each. A chart quadrat is one which is charted on paper and the position of each plant in the quadrat is shown. A denuded quadrat is one from which

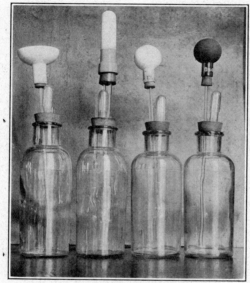

Fig. 118.—Various types of porous clay-cup atmometers.

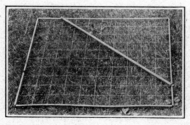

Fig. 119.—A portable folding quadrat divided into decimeter squares by means of cords.

the vegetation has been removed, while a permanent quadrat is one that is staked out so that observations may be made on it from year to year. Sometimes in studying vegetation a transect is found to be more useful than quadrats. A transect is a line drawn through a plant community and usually the plants along one side or along both sides of the line are listed.

One way of using the quadrat method in class work is as follows: 6 or 8 100-foot steel surveyor's tapes and about the same number of 10-foot tapes are provided, the number depending upon the size of the class. When a place for mapping has been selected 4 of the long tapes are used to lay out a quadrat 100 feet square, steel tent-pins being used to hold the tapes. A fifth tape is now stretched 10 feet from one side of the quadrat in such a way as to lay off a 10-foot strip. The short tapes are used to subdivide this strip into 10-foot quadrats. A party of about three students works on each 10-foot quadrat, two counting the plants and the third serving as recorder. Quadrat paper, ruled into 100 squares, each square representing a 10-foot quadrat, is used for the record. A combination of the chart and list quadrat is made. A symbol, usually an initial letter, is used for each species and a list of the species with their symbols is placed on the margin of the quadrat paper. The symbol of each species, with the number of individuals representing it, is placed within the quadrat space in which it occurs. Thus when the entire 100-foot quadrat is finished the record contains a list of all species found, the number of individuals of each species, and the position of each plant within 10 feet of its actual occurrence. From such a study students may readily determine the dominant species, the subdominant species of societies, and other structural characteristics of the community.

The quadrat method may also be used for determining the frequency of occurrence of the various species of a community. This may be done by using a folding meter quadrat, though some workers prefer a smaller size and some prefer a circle instead of a quadrat. This quadrat is placed in the vegetation and the species occurring in it are listed, the process being repeated at more or less regular intervals throughout the community. The result is that lists are obtained for a large number of small quadrats scattered through the community, the number depending upon the size of the community and the character of the vegetation. The next step is to determine in how many quadrats each species occurs. The dominant species may occur in all of them but most of the secondary species will not. The percentage of the total number of quadrats used in which a given species occurs is taken as the frequency index of that species. For example, if the total number of quadrats is 200 and a given species is found to occur in 72 of them, the frequency index of this species is 0.36.

Suggested Problems.

1. To make a map of the vegetation of a limited area.
2. To compare a climax association with a seral association as to number of species and number of individual plants.
3. To discover which species occur most frequently in a given association.
4. To study the revegetation of a denuded quadrat.

The Structure and Local Distribution of Plant Communities. — The quadrat method may be used for studying the structure of associations but a great deal may also be done by observation alone. In most localities a considerable amount of time can be given to this phase of the work. In this as in all ecological work it is necessary for the students to know the names of the plants concerned and there is always a question as to how much time should be devoted to systematic or taxonomic studies. The amount varies with the total amount of time available for class use but as a rule the ability to use keys for plant determination should be acquired in other courses rather than in ecology. At any rate it is much better to simply tell the students what the plants are than to sacrifice real ecological studies to the work of identification.

SUGGESTED PROBLEMS.

1. To discover how many layers of vegetation may be found in a forest and to determine the subdominant species of each.

2. To discover what plant societies are present in certain local associations.

3. To describe in detail the structure of a given association.

4. To compare "uplands" and "bottomlands" as to characteristic tree species.

5. To discover whether there is any correlation between soil types and the local distribution of vegetation.

Plant Succession.—The studies that may be made on plant succession will vary greatly with local conditions. Usually some early stages can be found on rock outcrops or on areas that have been denuded by erosion or by man, perhaps in the construction of a drainage ditch, or some other agency. Even an ant-hill or the soil thrown out around a woodchuck hole may be made to serve a valuable purpose. Usually also some examples of "zonation" may be found, each zone of vegetation representing a stage in a sere. This is especially well shown around ponds or lakes but may frequently be found also along streams. If coal-mining striplands, or sand-dune areas, or rock ravines, are available the class will be unusually fortunate.

SUGGESTED PROBLEMS.

1. To work out the hydrosere of an inland lake.

2. To discover what plants are the pioneer species on bare rock.

3. To outline the succession that takes place on an area denuded by the activity of man.

4. To compare a psammosere with a lithosere in the same climatic region.

5. To determine the successional significance of zonation.

Phenology.—As a general rule phenological studies are not well adapted for single field exercises but they furnish an abundance of excellent problems for individual students or groups of students to carry on throughout a field season.

Suggested Problems.

1. To make a study of the seasonal succession of flowers in a local association.

2. To make a comparative phenological record of all species of maple that are available.

3. To make a comparative study of the time of leaf development on the various species of trees on the campus or in a local wood-lot.

4. To make a comparative study of the time of leaf fall on the above trees.

5. To make a comparative study of the time of ripening of fruits on the plants of a local association.

References.

Bates, Carlos G. and Zon, Raphael: Research Methods in the Study of Forest Environment, U. S. Dept. Agr. Bull., 1922, **1059**, 208.

Clements, Frederic E. and Goldsmith, Glen W.: The Phytometer Method in Ecology: the Plant and Community as Instruments, Carnegie Inst. Washington Publ., 1924, **256**, III + 106 p., 11 pl., 45 fig.

Tansley, A. G., and Chipp, T. F.: Aims and Methods in the Study of Vegetation, The British Empire Vegetation Committee and the Crown Agents for the Colonies, London, 1926, **15** + 384 p., 62 fig.

INDEX.

A